THE SEVEN SECRETS OF SOMEWHERE LAKE

The Seven Secrets of Somewhere Lake

Animal Ways that
Inspire and Amaze

by

SAM CAMPBELL
The Philosopher of the Forest

ILLUSTRATED BY HARRY H. LEES

PACIFIC PRESS PUBLISHING ASSOCIATION
Mountain View, California
Omaha, Nebraska   Oshawa, Ontario

To

CARL MARTY, JR.

Friend of All Animals

CONTENTS

CONTENTS—*Continued*

THE SEVEN SECRETS OF SOMEWHERE LAKE

I

NO BABY ANIMALS

SALT and Pepper, the grizzled old porcupines, were forest veterans capable of taking care of themselves, and they appeared quite conscious and proud of this fact. They waddled awkwardly across the forest floor carrying on their little grunty talk, their thousands of quills rustling at each step. Then Salt slowly climbed a good-sized maple tree while Pepper chose an oak. Through the thin early-spring foliage we could see them making their way upward.

"That's the way I want them to be," I said to Giny as we watched their deliberate movements. "They are independent of us and fully capable of taking care of themselves."

"So it is with our raccoons, chipmunks, squirrels, deer, birds and everybody," added Giny with something of a sigh. "I suppose it must be that way, but I am not so sure I like it."

She interposed a few porcupine calls that made our famous pets stop their climbing and look down. "You old rascals!" she said to them. "I still miss the days when you were babies chewing on our furniture, biting my fingers, setting quills in my hands, and pestering from morning to night. Did you have to grow up and get so wrapped up in your life in the woods that all you will do is give us a passing greeting?"

"But don't you see, dear," I interposed, "all things happen in proper order. When we had the time to take care of baby animals we had lots of them. We could give them proper attention. Now this summer——"

"Yes, I know—this summer we will see little of our home," she interrupted. "I don't like that either. There is nothing else I love as much as our cabin, especially when it is filled with baby animals. Remember Rack and Ruin, the raccoons, when they were little tikes? Did you ever see anything cuter than Eeny, Meeny, Miney, Mo and Still-Mo, the red squirrels?—or the woodchucks? Oh, I shall miss them terribly!"

"But doesn't it thrill you to know that we are going to the Grand Canyon?" I persisted, not feeling very sure of myself. "In the Kaibab Forest there are almost as many animals as trees. We will see the famous white-tailed black squirrel, the black-tailed mule deer, bear and I promise, I *vow* that I will show you a mountain lion."

Giny sighed again. "Well—I suppose I'll like it once I get started. But it means no baby animals and that is a high price to pay, even for the Grand Canyon." Giny was adjusting herself to our plans, but she was far from content.

"Of course, we can't have baby animals this summer," I said in a matter-of-fact tone. "We couldn't possibly raise them to the point where they were able to take care of themselves before we left."

"No baby animals," Giny echoed, still weighing the cost.

"NO BABY ANIMALS!" I reaffirmed, as a last word.

We were walking up the trail to our cabin as we talked. On the limb of a birch tree sat our treasured friend Cheer, the red-winged blackbird. Giny held out some peanut crumbs to him and he hopped to her hand and helped himself, calling his happy *"Cheer, Cheer"* as he did. Mite, the mighty chickadee, came fluttering up for his share, and so did Nutty, the nuthatch.

Giny hadn't given up yet. Inside the cabin she opened the subject again. "What are you going to do if some baby animals are brought to you for care?" she asked. "It happens every year. You couldn't just turn them away."

"Someone else will care for them," I said confidently. "After all, this world was rolling along before you and I came into it. We haven't any monopoly on kindness or love of animals. Ray and Ada will take in any living creature, and so will Merl." I was referring to some of our north-woods neighbors.

"That's true, but animals they raised wouldn't be ours, they wouldn't be living right here and making this their home so we would have them in the future. Do you feel sure Hi-Bub would not come and stay while we are away?"

I was silent before this suggestion and I guess my expression reflected a certain heaviness of thought. "You are concerned about Hi-Bub, aren't you?" said Giny understandingly. "Do you think he has changed so extremely?"

Yes, I was concerned about that fine young lad we knew as Hi-Bub. Ever since he was a rosy-cheeked, lisping child he had been an important part of our lives. Though not related by blood, we felt him close as a son. He had lived with us, hiked the Sanctuary trails, been with us on

silent canoe journeys along the lake shores and had gone into the distant Canadian woods with us in search of adventure. Always his dynamic enthusiasm could be counted on to enliven our experiences. His energy was boundless and his love for nature infectious.

Then he went to a large city to school. At first his

letters reflected the enthusiasm we had loved. But after a few months the letters were shorter and less frequent. The language became restrained, the feeling strange and distant. One evening but a few weeks back we had dinner at his home. In a very few minutes we realized something had happened to Hi-Bub. Privately his father said to me, "Hi-Bub has changed and we are worried. I cannot find out what is affecting him. He won't talk of it. Month after month we have seen him becoming sober and serious until he seldom enters into any kind of fun. He acts as if he were carrying the burdens of the world."

"We first noticed how quiet and preoccupied he was becoming," declared his mother. "Then the big shock came when he announced that he was changing the course of his education—he wants to major in *business administration!*"

Hi-Bub majoring in business administration! It was inconceivable. Not that there is anything wrong with business administration—it is a most admirable career for those suited to it. But such a field of endeavor didn't fit Hi-Bub any more than feathers fit a frog. If there ever was a natural naturalist it was this lad, and it was impossible for me to picture him trading lodges for ledgers, journeys for journals, pistils for pencils, pines for papers, tents for trivials, and the timeless pattern of the forest for time clocks!

"Maybe he should come up to our Sanctuary again this summer," I commented, much concerned. "The woods will reach his heart if anything can."

Later Hi-Bub refused our invitation. He was planning

to go to summer school, he said. He thought he might finish high school in three years instead of the usual four.

"We don't want him to finish in three years," declared his mother. "We want him to remain a boy and enjoy these precious years."

When we arrived north it seemed to Giny and me that we were never quite free of the memory of this visit with Hi-Bub.

"Hi-Bub does not want to come, Giny," I said. "We must face that fact."

"But I am sure it is not because he loves us or the woods any the less." Giny's confidence in Hi-Bub was unshaken.

"Yes, I am equally sure of it," I agreed. "Apparently he alone is conscious of the nature of his problem and he alone can solve it. We can help him by knowing he is equal to it whatever it may be, and certainly we will be awaiting him when he comes out the far side. In the meantime, it is clear that we cannot count on him this summer."

"No baby animals!" sighed Giny.

"No! NO BABY ANIMALS!" I snapped conclusively.

II

ZIPPER!

IT WAS the first day of June, but one would never have guessed it from the looks of the world. Snow was falling. Or maybe it was raining, it was difficult to tell which. Great gray flakes drifted down, so heavy they hit the ground with a thud. Little maple buds caught some of the flakes and made them into saucy hats. The forest was wet and soggy, the air wore a chilling cold.

In the midst of this a workman arrived at our island bringing our mail. On top of a stack of letters rested a post card of nondescript handwriting. How it ever reached me was hard to understand. It was addressed to "Mister Camible Sam."

"Der Mister Sir" it began, and then two thirds of the way down we made out "I am got truble. What Im gonna do?" Then there were some scratchings which even the FBI couldn't have figured out, followed by four words "plese cum queek, plese." Giny finally determined that it was signed "Old Pete."

"Why should Old Pete be writing to you?" she asked. "He hasn't liked you very well, has he?"

"Oh, I think he likes me all right," I replied. "And I like Pete. We just don't agree on certain things, that's all."

Pete was an old trapper. He had lived in the woods all

17

his life, worked as a lumberjack during the early days of
the region, and when this industry moved on, he settled
down in a crude cabin to live off the forest. With him
dwelt two grown sons, Ed and Bill. All three were thorns
in the side of the law. They hunted and trapped without
reason or season. If they were caught they cared little,
for jail meant free board and room. In their philosophy
the animals of the forest were for their use. Laws to protect those creatures they regarded as an unjust interfer-
ence with their natural rights. Conservation was too big a
word for them to say, much less understand. Since I
had been an advocate of conservation, I symbolized all
that opposed their freedom and life in the forest.

"Why would Pete send for you?" Giny was asking.
"He has other neighbors much nearer."

"I don't know," I replied. "Anyway I'm going to him.
Want to come along?"

Giny did, and soon we were bumping over ruts and
sliding through mud holes as our car struggled down the
serpentine road that led to Pete's cabin. We went over a
rickety bridge that spanned Heron Creek and brought us
into view of their crude backwoods home.

"It is pure flattery to call that a cabin," said Giny, as
we sighted the place through the trees. "That is a shack
if ever there was one."

Shack it was! It was made of logs that were decaying
under long years of wear and lack of care. Sphagnum
moss from a near-by swamp had been used to chink the
widening cracks. The roof had several colors of tar
paper, and the chimney that led up from a wood-burning

stove tilted carelessly to one side. The yard was mussy. Near the door stood the disorderly remains of a wood pile that had barely stretched to spring. An old minnow seine leaned against the cabin wall, and hanging on nails driven into trees were a number of steel traps. The sight of such traps always sends chills down my spine.

"Is it possible that men can live in such a place?" asked Giny incredulously.

Her answer came from the cabin itself. From the door emerged three men, who had heard the approach of our car. First was Old Pete himself, dressed in a faded wool shirt dotted with rips and moth holes, and a pair of trousers that looked like a mail bag. A thick mat of whiskers covered his face up to his temples. He may have been smiling for all we knew, but we could never have seen it behind all that facial foliage.

Next came Ed, a slender man in his late twenties, dressed as untidily as his father. Bill followed, furnishing Giny with quite a surprise. He wore a neat, new shirt, trousers that had never taken part in the skinning of a muskrat, and shoes that had at least on occasion made acquaintance with polish and brush. He was shaved and his hair carefully combed.

"Can he belong to them?" Giny whispered, as the men approached the car. "He looks so different."

"Bill is an enigma!" I whispered back, as rapidly as possible. "Don't be carried away by his manners—as 'most everyone is. He acts the part of sincerity—makes you think he is on your side. But he can't be trusted. It was he who trapped our pet coyote and our wildcat—sold them for the bounty. He doesn't know that I know it, but I do. He was the one who cleaned out that beaver house on Four Mile Creek. Drove a pipe into the house in the middle of winter, poured ether in, then, while the animals were unconscious, he broke open the roof and got them. Yet, he does some fine things too. He has searched all night to find a man lost in the woods, risked his life to save people from fire, and——"

"Sh-h-h, here he is," interrupted Giny.

Bill had walked up to the car, wearing a smile of welcome that was positively disarming. "Welcome, friends!" he said strongly, opening the car door for Giny. "So good of you to come. Careful, Mrs. Campbell, don't step in that mud."

"Thank you," returned Giny as he helped her from the car. "You are Bill, aren't you? I am glad to see you."

"Yes, I'm Bill, and this is my father, Pete, and my brother, Ed."

Giny greeted them. I came around the car to receive a pump-handle handshake from Pete, a quick sharp grip from Ed and a two-handed clasp from Bill. I returned the cordiality earnestly. How I wanted to like that fellow Bill, to believe in his pretensions. But there was the feeling that his manners, like the rusty steel contraptions hanging on the tree, were a snare.

"Well, Pete," I said when the greetings were finished. "We got your card. What can we do for you?"

"You cum tak heem?" asked Pete.

"Take him? Who?"

"Zipper," interposed Bill. "Didn't he tell you about Zipper?"

"Maybe that was the line on the post card I couldn't read," I answered. "Now, who in the world is Zipper?"

"You cum," grunted Pete from behind his whiskers, and he led us to the back of his cabin. It was snowing again now and wet flakes were clinging to Pete's bushy hair, but he heeded them not.

We rounded the cabin and came to a stop before the sorriest sight I have seen in the forest. There stood Zipper, a very young fawn, looking like an unfinished statue of "Despair." She seemed to have got the wrong set of bones. They wouldn't fit inside her speckled hide. Her ribs showed through in even ridges. Her hip bones were about to puncture the skin, and you could count her vertebrae from her big ears to her white-tipped tail. Her head drooped, and about her neck was a rope big enough to haul a Mississippi scow.

"You poor little thing!" exclaimed Giny.

"Por theeng, Mrs. Camp*bell?*" queried Old Pete, with unnecessary acent on the last syllable of the name. "He not por theeng now! You shu see heem wen I fin'—wen I peck heem up hees bone rattle. He no can stan'! He no can eat! I mak' heem—I pok' eat down hees troat."

Bill tried to explain in better language. "Pete found the fawn in a ditch beside the road," he said. "Something had happened to the doe." (I wondered just what *had* happened!) "The little fellow was in a bad way. Pete brought him home. We had to tie him up for fear he would wander away and the wolves get him. But he didn't want to be tied. We would just get him set, and zip—he would jerk his head out of the rope. That's why we called him Zipper. This big rope holds him someway."

In spite of the pronouns the men used, Zipper was a young female. She had one feature that redeemed her from the appearance of utter tragedy—her eyes. The

way they flashed testified that she wasn't defeated and wasn't going to be.

"What do you feed her, Pete?" asked Giny, advancing slowly toward the fawn. The creature backed away to the limit of the rope, the big loop slipped to a bony point just back of her ears and held firmly while she tugged vainly for freedom. An area on her neck from which the hair was worn away showed that she had tried this often before.

"Ho, I geev heem potato, somtam onion, pancake, an' what you know—he lak tobacco!"

"Tobacco!" I exclaimed. "Pete, Pete—you shouldn't give her tobacco."

"Ya, I know," agreed Pete. "Tobacco, he cos' money."

"Well, what this fawn needs is milk and lots of it," I said, skipping a temptation to laugh at Pete's reasoning.

Old Pete looked at me incredulously. Milk? Why he hadn't had any milk in ten years. Bill and Ed laughed, and one said something about it being so far to town they never bothered to get milk.

In the meantime, Giny had succeeded in getting up to the fawn. After several hopeless tugs at the rope, the creature submitted to her petting.

"Ah, you lak heem—he lak you," observed Old Pete, with some show of enthusiasm.

"Pete!" I said meaningfully.

"Ya, ya," agreed the old trapper. "I fergit he's a her."

While Giny slowly gained the confidence of Zipper, likely showing the young creature the first tenderness it had ever known, I drew forth the facts from the three men. Plainly, they had the fawn and didn't know what to do with it. They wanted us to take it home.

"What I'm gonna do?" exclaimed Pete. "Dees little fella, all bones, not good for eat."

Zipper, give thanks you're skinny, I thought, then I said, "In other words, boys, you want me to take Zipper home and care for her—is that it?"

Old Pete whistled through his whiskers, "You tak heem?"

"Yes, but it is a doe, Pete."

"Ya, he's a her."

Bill walked over beside the fawn. "She isn't getting the right food here," he said to Giny. "We can't take care of her. We know you folks understand raising such animals."

Zipper wasn't so sure she wanted anyone doing things for her—if by that was meant being stuck in the back seat of an automobile. The fact that it was a new car made no difference to her. The moment it was plain to her what we intended to do, she forgot about being a "poor thing," as Giny had been calling her, and she began behaving like a Hottentot. She jerked at her rope, bleated like a lamb, kicked with her bony legs and butted with her head. She set Old Pete down in a mud puddle, tore Bill's new shirt and knocked the grin off Ed's face. I succeeded in lifting her off the ground, but I felt as if I had a fur-covered earthquake in my arms. While I held on desperately, Ed grabbed the two front feet, Bill the two back ones, and we eased her into the car. Once inside, she was more calm, though she managed to scratch her autograph on everything that had a varnish coating.

"Good-by, Zipper," called Bill as we started away. "I hope next time I see you, you are a big fat doe."

Heaven help you if you are, I thought.

" 'By," said Ed.

"Ya," said Old Pete.

"Thanks for Zipper," called Giny.

"Thanks for taking her," answered Bill. "Mind if I come over and see her sometime?"

"No, come whenever you wish," Giny returned.

I didn't know how much of that message reached the ears of Bill, for we were lurching and bumping over that miserable forest road. Zipper was bleating, and Giny was trying to comfort her, while I did enough steering to take a car halfway across the continent on a regular highway.

"Are you sure Bill is such an undependable fellow?" asked Giny, when at last we reached a paved road and words were possible.

"Isn't it easy to like him?" I asked, judging that Giny was impressed by his manners. "Several times I have been completely convinced that he had reformed. Yet, the game warden says he is the most persistent violator in the country."

Giny was thoughtful for a moment. Then she said, "Well, I hope he does come over to see Zipper."

"You'd better put a bulletproof vest on Zipper when he comes," I replied skeptically.

On our way back we stopped at the home of the conservation warden to obtain his permission to care for the fawn. All game belongs to the state, and the wardens give careful supervision to all animals. Particularly have they been watchful of fawns during recent years. People unacquainted with the ways of deer sometimes pick up a newborn fawn, not knowing that the little thing has been purposely left by the mother and that she will come back. Thus the young deer is robbed of the mother's milk, the best possible food for it, and the doe suffers because her milk is not relieved. One look at Zipper and the warden knew that the story of this fawn was different. We could care for it, he said, so long as it was not confined.

We reached our landing anticipating a terrific job to get Zipper from the car into the boat. Whether she was exhausted or not, I cannot say, but she behaved like a well-trained dog. She still had the heavy rope on her neck, and as we tugged slightly on it she came out of the car, walked to the boat and climbed in. She stayed fairly quiet until we reached the island. There we removed the rope and set her free.

"Now!" exclaimed Giny, tossing the rope to one side. "Zipper, you're never going to wear that overgrown necktie again!"

Zipper rolled her eyes, looking as if she couldn't believe the thing was gone. Suddenly she jumped right up in the air, whirled and ran off through the brush. We could hear her breaking twigs at the far side of the island. In a minute she was back again, pausing near us to do the silliest steps, ducking her head, pawing the ground, starting a few steps in one direction then sharply changing her course, until Giny and I were in near hysterics from laughing.

"Hi-O, Zipper!" I called. "You are home, little girl, you are home. No more ropes, no more onions or potato peelings."

Giny hastened to get Zipper some milk. Presently she came out with a baby's bottle full and capped with a nipple for Zipper's convenience.

Zipper paused in her hectic play. She looked at Giny curiously. The bottle was a new idea; she knew her onions, but what kind of food was this? Giny touched her nose with the nipple, then put it to her lips. She shook her little head a bit. Then she chanced to lick with her tongue and to get a taste of the milk. Cautiously she took the nipple. A most peculiar look came into her eyes. She gave an excited little bleat, and then began the most violent eating I have ever witnessed. She tugged at the nipple until she stretched it twice its normal length. She jerked so hard Giny could barely hold onto the bottle.

When Zipper was satisfied, Giny went about preparing dinner for us. I sank into a chair in somewhat of a daze. Giny was singing a little song of her own composition, and I finally made out the words, "No baby animals! No baby animals! No baby animals this year!"

III

ZOWIE!

SNOW can come in June in the north country, but it can't stay long. While gray skies remain, winter's confetti may strew the ground, mingle with violets and spring beauties, cap the stumps and rest on balsam branches; but let the clouds break and the spring sun have a look, and the unseasonable visitors dissolve into drops and rivulets.

So it was with our June snow the day Zipper moved into the Sanctuary. After a few hours, the sun broke through the overcast and shone strong, bright, warm and cheery. Under its touch buds swelled on the maples and oaks, catkins lengthened on the aspen trees, the polygola, pipsissewa and wild lily of the valley smiled up from the forest floor, and the lake sparkled with countless diamonds.

Zipper took time out from running to sun herself. It seemed to us that she looked better already. I had been to town and laid in a stock of the best food I could find, including Pablum. She was hungry perpetually and we had to exercise considerable restraint to keep from overfeeding her. Never had we seen such an energetic fawn.

"She does everything but fly," exclaimed Giny as we were watching the fawn race about. "About two more vitamins and she'll do that!"

Zipper was exuberantly happy in her island home and

new liberty. One morning we watched her clowning. Giny had just given Zipper a full bottle of milk which the fawn drank in her usual violent manner. After swallowing the last drop and trying to take the nipple and bottle in also, she walked slowly away. In a spot of sunlight she paused for a moment. Then a complete change of expression came into her eyes. Did she compare the dinner she had just eaten to onions, potatoes and scraps? Did she suddenly realize how grand it was to be free from that hauser about her neck? Whatever inspired her, in an instant she became a three-ringed circus all rolled into one. She tossed her head from side to side in a silly manner, then jumped straight up in the air, all four feet off the ground.

We laughed until we couldn't laugh any more.

"Zipper, you are destined for the ballet," exclaimed Giny when she could talk. "Oh, how I wish Hi-Bub could see that!"

"Yes indeed," I agreed. "That would draw him out of himself, I do believe." Then I sobered. "By the way," I said, "do you have any definite idea as to what we are going to do with Zipper? It is less than a month until we start west to Grand Canyon. She couldn't take care of herself."

"Well," said Giny, "You thought Ada and Ray, or Merl would take in some animals. One look at Zipper and they would want her."

"Yes," I pouted, "then when we come back, Zipper would be theirs—she would be accustomed to their grounds . . . ."

"Round and round we go," said Giny. "I've been thinking in that circle ever since Zipper arrived. Let's not think about it now. Come on there, you beautiful little clown," she called to the fawn, running toward it and clapping her hands. "Do some more of your crazy stunts."

And Zipper did. Suddenly the air was filled with laughter, and it wasn't our own. There were deep-throated haw-haws from down near the lake shore.

"Ya, the leetle fella he is craze!" called a voice we recognized, and we looked down to see Old Pete, Ed and Bill standing there watching Zipper. They had crossed to the island in a boat we kept on the mainland for the convenience of visitors.

"Hello there, you three," I called.

"Come on up," added Giny. "If you came to see Zipper, you arrived at the right time."

"Ya, ya," exclaimed Old Pete. "He go like . . ." and the old trapper imitated the fawn the best he could, shaking his head from side to side and jumping all of two inches off the ground.

"Here, Pops," said Bill, laying a restraining hand on Old Pete's shoulder, "better save that pep for the wood-pile." The three men walked up to us as they talked.

"He lak himself here more better," declared Pete.

"Pete," I said, "that is a young doe."

"Ya, ya—he's a her."

We showed our surprise guests about the cabin and the island. Then they revealed the real object of their visit.

"Over east of us Tom Henderson has a farm," Bill said. "He caught a fox in a trap, and found a young one beside the dead mother. He took him home to make a pet of him—but now he is afraid the fox will kill his chickens. And he decided to kill the fox."

"Kill him?" echoed Giny. "Kill him after he had made a pet of him?"

"Well, Tom tried to send him away and he wouldn't go," Bill went on. "He took him away back in the woods and he was home the next day. So, he said he would have to kill him."

"Don't let him do that," pleaded Giny. "Bill, you get the fox and take him somewhere. He has a right to live."

"Ya, ya," said Old Pete. "Bill tak heem some plas— he bring heem here."

"Here?" I questioned.

"Here?" echoed Giny.

"Well, I thought maybe you would keep him on your island until he could take care of himself," explained Bill. "I have him in a box down in the boat. Want to see him?"

"No," I broke in desperately. "Bill, I can't take baby animals this year. I don't know what to do with Zipper. I don't want even to see that fox."

"It wouldn't do any harm just to look at him," said Giny excitedly. "Is it a gray fox or a red one?"

"Red fox," said Bill with his winning smile. He shot a challenging side glance at me. "Wait, I'll bring him up." He went to the boat and returned in a moment carrying a crude crate. We peeked through cracks between the boards and there saw a bright-eyed, sharp-eared, red fox pup.

"Would he let me pet him?" Giny asked.

"Sure!" said Bill. "He likes to be petted."

The fox lay perfectly still as the lid was opened, and soon Giny was stroking his rich red fur, calling him all the endearing names in the dictionary.

I shall never know just what happened in the next minute, except I strongly suspect that Bill was responsible. Zipper came by, and our attention was drawn from the fox. Suddenly the crate slipped from Bill's hands and fell to the ground. The fox was out and gone at lightning speed. It would be a misstatement to say he ran away—nothing could run like that. He was just a blurred red streak that disappeared into the brush.

"Zowie!" I shouted. "Look at that fellow go."

"Zowie is right," exclaimed Giny.

"Zowie—hees a good name," shouted Old Pete.

Bill and Ed ran after the fox. Again and again the graceful creature flitted across our field of vision, at last vanishing under our woodshed. Soon we were all on our hands and knees looking into the dark recesses under the building, where at the very limit of the light we could see two sharp-pointed ears and two shining eyes. There that fox stayed, and all the coaxing and argument we could put forth didn't cause him to budge.

"Well, it looks as if you had a fox," said Bill.

"Bill," I said, narrowing my eyes, "if there was a bounty on your hide I'd collect it right now. What do you suppose I am going to do?"

"Ya, ya," Old Pete was saying. He was on his knees, looking under the shed. "Zowie, she's move in for stay."

And stay Zowie did. Old Pete and his two sons left presently after taking one last look under the shed where the fox still lay serenely.

I went into the cabin and dropped into a chair. First Zipper and now Zowie had been tossed into my lap. What was I going to do? "If only Hi-Bub were here," I murmured.

"Right now there is something going on outdoors you ought to see," broke in Giny. "Take a look out the window."

I did and beheld Zipper and Zowie standing about five feet from each other, pointing nose to nose like two bird dogs. Then they started a very cautious advance, front feet inching forward while their hind feet remained stationary. Farther and farther they stretched until their noses just about touched. There they stood, each asking the other, "What in the world are you, Democrat or Republican?"

But the strain was too much for Zipper. She shook her head and executed one of her famous jumps right up in the air. Zowie, frightened all the way to the tip of his fluffy tail, turned a backward flip and raced away. Zipper ran in the opposite direction. Two minutes later they both came back, timidly peered out of the brush at each other and started the whole maneuver again. This was supreme comedy!

A little later as I sat reading, I heard Giny calling from outside, "Oh, Sam! Oh, Sam! Zowie is here and he is taking food from my hand. . . . Now he is letting me scratch his ears. . . . Now I am stroking his back. . . ." Then she said, all for my benefit, "Too bad, Zowie, you can't be a baby animal. But, you see, Sam says we can't have any baby animals this year. So you can't be a little three-month-old fox with red fur, a sharp nose, sharp-pointed ears and star-like eyes. If you are going to stay here, you have to be a great big rhinocerpuss, or something!"

IV

ZANIE!

OUR letter to Hi-Bub had been a little strained. We wrote every detail of our experience in acquiring the fox and fawn, and each event was enlarged somewhat in the telling.

Then came the answer—quickly to be sure, but the very envelope carried a suggestion of disappointment. It was addressed to Mr. and Mrs. Sam Campbell, instead of Sam and Giny Campbell. He wrote:

Dear Friends, Thank you for telling me about Zipper and Zowie. They must be beautiful animals. I wish I might see them, but I guess such things are not for me now. I shall always cling to the happy memories I have of the Sanctuary, and I am grateful to you for them.

The letter immediately went into brief mention of his schooling and carried a greeting from his parents.

"Sounds almost like a last will and testament," said Giny.

"I can't escape the feeling that he is acting a part," I said with conviction. "This isn't Hi-Bub."

"Well, what should we do? What can we do?" Giny evidenced her concern.

I walked to the window and looked out. The forest bristled with life.

"I have seen the north woods work wonders with boys in helping them through mental messes," I declared. "Whatever it is that is burdening our lad, it is unnatural and it doesn't belong to him. Let's give him large doses of the woods."

"Sounds like a right idea," agreed Giny. "That is, if we can get him to take the doses we offer. . . . Look!"

Giny grasped my arm and directed my attention to a commotion out in the woods. Low balsam and cedar trees were being shaken by the action of some animal. In a moment, out of the brush walked our two porcupines, Salt and Pepper, their under parts still dripping from a swim in the lake. It was a moment we had been hoping for and yet dreading. The periodic visits of these two grizzled old porkies were thrilling to us. They had been gone from the island for a few days. In the meantime Zipper and Zowie came. We were wondering, with some measure of concern, what would happen when these animals met.

The answer was close at hand. Zipper and Zowie came racing about the house in one of their wild sprees. They were within a few feet of the porkies before they saw them. Zipper came to such a sudden halt that Zowie ran head first into her hind legs. Salt and Pepper came to a halt too, but it didn't make much disturbance, as they weren't going much faster than a turtle anyway. Up came their quills as they faced these two strangers.

There was a moment of suspended animation as the four animals faced one another. Then Zowie made a sad mistake: he snapped at Salt. With a marvelously quick move the porcupine swung his tail and connected with the fox, planting four quills in the tender flesh about his nose.

Immediately the scene was animated, everyone running somewhere. Zowie left for the south side of the island, Zipper to the north, and Salt and Pepper scuffled up separate trees.

Some time later I saw Zowie peering out from a bush, the painful quills still dangling. I coaxed and coaxed and finally got the disillusioned creature up to me. "You got away lucky," I assured him. "If that blow had hit you squarely, your nose would look like a cactus plant. These are easy. They are barely sticking in your skin."

With a quick move I jerked the quills from the fox's nose. A dog might have howled at this sudden pain, but not a fox. Wild creatures are prepared to endure suffering in silence. Zowie looked up at me with a startled expression, then jerked away and disappeared into the brush. He had learned his lesson. When he returned again, it was with much caution and considerable respect for porcupines. He had discovered that the world isn't all roses, that there are some thorns too.

Now there was more shopping to do, and when things had quieted down somewhat at the Sanctuary, Giny and I went to town. Salt and Pepper were asleep up two favorite trees, Zipper was curled up in some tall grass and Zowie had retired to his favorite spot under the shed. We crossed to the mainland and drove to town. The grocery list was headed by seven quarts of milk for Zipper; dog biscuits for Zowie and the raccoons; peanuts for the chipmunks and squirrels; grain for the chickadees, redwings, song sparrows and blue jays; and suet for the Canada jays. Somewhere near the bottom of the list were a few items for ourselves.

On the return from town we had a sudden notion to go a roundabout way over a road which we seldom used. It was a beautiful drive through a heavily wooded area. At one point where once a sawmill had operated was a small clearing bearing some resemblance to a farm. There were a house and a barn, a field where potatoes were hopefully planted, and a vegetable garden surrounded by a high fence designed to discourage deer from raiding the place.

As we were approaching this spot, I noticed a car some distance ahead of us come to a stop. A figure got out, placed something on the ground, then hurriedly got in again, and the car drove away. I kept studying this little "something" that had been placed beside the road. Obviously it was alive, very much alive, and when we reached the spot, it was racing all over the place. Here among the weeds and grasses at the side of the road was a taffy-colored pup, mostly of cocker-spaniel ancestry. He did not notice us in the least, his entire attention being devoted to a flock of fritillary butterflies that were fluttering about the weeds and flowers. While Giny and I laughed, he raced back and forth barking and barking until his tongue hung out so far we were afraid he would step on it.

"You can't chase all the butterflies in the world, you crazy little thing," Giny called when at last he dropped to the ground striving to regain his breath. She opened the car door and reached her hand toward the little fellow. Apparently accustomed to a car, he jumped right in and

climbed up on her lap, still panting from his exertion.

"Why, you blessed little thing!" Giny exclaimed. "I didn't invite you in. You stay out there until your folks come back for you." Her actions did not coincide with her words, for she was snuggling the pup up closely.

"I have a sneaking suspicion," I said, looking down the road in the direction the car had gone.

"What sort of a suspicion?" she asked.

"Well, I believe the people in that car do not intend to come back."

"You mean, they left this darling little pup—deliberately deserted him?"

I nodded. "Such things are done all too frequently," I said, still looking down the road. "It looks to me as if they dropped him near this farm figuring that those people would give him a home."

"But what if they didn't give him a home?" exclaimed Giny incredulously. "What would happen to this little fellow in the woods? What could make people do such a thing?"

"They use many excuses," I replied. "Often a pet is more trouble than people expect it to be. Every year there are many cats and dogs dropped from cars like that and left on their own in the forest."

Giny was in a mock battle with the little cocker. He took her hand in his mouth, growling fiercely, while he rolled his eyes up at her to see if he were biting too hard.

"What happens to dogs and cats deserted in the forest that way?" asked Giny, giving the pup a hug that brought a grunt from him.

"It is one of the meanest things anyone can do," I replied. "Cats become destroyers of birds and small game. Many times they end up caught in a steel trap. Dogs sometimes become wild and necessarily live off the forest. Large dogs become deer killers."

"Horrible!" exclaimed Giny, but she couldn't say more, for the pup was carried away with the enthusiasm of his play. Now he was jumping right up in Giny's face, his little eyes flashing with excitement. Right up on her shoulders he scrambled, then on top of her head, next across the back of the seat and onto my shoulders, biting my ears, pawing at my hair, and acting like a canine tornado. "You little imp," Giny said, boxing with him while he scrambled about the back of my neck. "You're positively zanie!"

The pup's answer was to jump right out into space in her direction without any regard for where he might land. He finished on the car floor, the wind jolted out of him for a minute, and lay there all sprawled out, tail wagging (what there was of it), big eyes dancing, and his tongue out about four inches.

"Zanie is right," I agreed. "He's the craziest thing I ever saw on four legs."

"What are we going to do with him?" Giny was stroking his head.

"Maybe the people at that little farm would take him." I was looking back at the place.

"Yes, and they would put him on a chain—or a big rope like Old Pete used on Zipper!"

"How do you know they would?"

"Oh, I can tell by the looks of the place. See that tumble-down barn? Doesn't that tell you that Zanie would be tied up? And he would have to eat potato peelings and onions, and nobody would play with him. Then when he barked they would make him lie down and keep quiet. Pretty soon he would lose his spirit and he wouldn't do crazy things any more. He wouldn't be Zanie."

"Looks as if you had named him," I said, getting a few pats in on my own account. "Zanie, you're a beautiful little problem. What are we going to do with you?"

Zanie licked my hand and smiled a doggy grin.

"We can find a better home for him than that!" assured Giny, picking the pup off the floor and cuddling him in her lap. "Let's take him home and . . ."

"Giny!" I said sharply, glaring at her.

"Yes, Sam."

I looked from her to the dog and back again, knowing full well that I couldn't refuse either one of them what they were asking with all their hearts. "Would you close the car door please, so Zanie doesn't fall out?"

As we drove along toward the Sanctuary, Giny set the squirming pup on her knee, holding him so she could look right into his beaming face. "Zanie," she said for my benefit. "You are going to meet Zipper, the big old Whiffenpoof, and Zowie, the Rhinocerpuss. These are great big fierce beasts and very, very old. And you can't be a baby animal either. Oh, dear no! You are a terrific old Hodag. Zanie, the Hodag—that's you!"

"*Arff!*" said Zanie.

V

ZINNIA!

JUST what is a dog anyway? Of what stuff is the little critter made that he can become so important in our lives and see so much importance in us? You can't explain it all in terms of what is found between the tip of his tail and the end of his nose and in the provisions of his pedigree. There is a certain regal authority about a dog, any dog. His position in the human scheme is not attained; it is traditionally or maybe divinely conferred. His is the right to curl up at our firesides, to stand guard at our doors, to trail us as we walk over the countryside, to love us and give us something to love. Perchance he may chew up a slipper or two, or a favorite rug, just to prove he is worthy of forgiveness. He is commissioned to mellow our sorrows, enhance our joys, and teach us in an original doggy sort of way the meaning of devotion, loyalty and sincerity.

Zanie moved into our Sanctuary with ease and authority. His selected post from the first hour was on the front step, where he draped himself gracefully, two front feet hanging over the edge, while he looked about for all that is good and interesting and at the same time guarded against all that is evil.

In that hour we learned that our pup friend had a prankster's sense of humor. If he were human instead of canine, he would have been the sort of practical joker who loves to put tacks on chairs, pepper on stoves, and poke snow down girls' necks. He was just six pounds of mischief, all done up in such a beautiful hide and gifted with such cute manners, happy smile, lovely eyes and sweet disposition that he could get away with anything.

He found out Giny did not want him on her bed. A dozen times she put him down, a dozen times he jumped up again. She scolded him, and he barked back. She shook him, he tried to shake her. She spanked him, very lightly, and he licked her hand. Tiring of this, he grabbed Giny's favorite Navajo rug, one she had bought from the Indian weavers in the far Southwest. With a vicious growl, he started to shake it.

"No, no, Zanie!" exclaimed Giny. "No, not that."

That was all he wanted to know. If that rug was something he shouldn't have, then it was exactly what he wanted. Under the bed he dragged it, fighting and growling as if he tusseled with a wildcat! Giny had hold of the rug, trying to get it away from him, but she didn't want to pull too hard. I crawled in from the other side of the bed and pushed on his wagging tail to relieve the strain. To Zanie this was wonderful. He was annoying two people instead of one and his enthusiasm knew no bounds. He sounded like a four-cornered dogfight. I pushed and Giny pulled and at last we had the little cyclone out in the open. We all paused to consider what to do. Zanie had his teeth sunk in the precious rug and he looked up at us as defiant as Ajax of the lightning. His eyes rolled from one of us to the other, flashing with a savage joy. He was in the center of doggy heaven.

"What can we do?" asked Giny anxiously. "I don't want to tear it."

"Suppose we just walk away," I suggested. "Maybe if we won't play, he won't either."

We walked away, but the ruse didn't fool that pup a bit. With a growl that was all out of proportion to his size, he whisked the rug under the bed again. He knew we would follow him, and we did. Giny dove under from one side, and I from the other. Once again I pushed on his wagging, stubby tail while she pulled on the rug. Then we were right back where we started, Giny and I standing looking down at him helplessly, while he closed his jaws all the tighter on the rug and looked up in impish hilarity, his tail oscillating at sixty miles an hour!

Then I tried a trick that usually makes a dog let go. While he growled in pretended savagery, I pinched his nostrils together, shutting off his breathing. Now his only way to get a breath was through his mouth, and that meant letting go his hold. I could tell by his expression that he understood the situation.

"You be ready to jerk the rug away," I cautioned Giny.

Oh, how that pup hated to give up! He was defeated and he knew it, but he held out to the last possible second. His eyes threatened me, and then they tried pleading with me. He even whined a little to work on sympathy, but I held on. He looked at Giny, but found no mercy there. His eyes rolled about the room—all that nice air, and he just had to get some of it. Suddenly he tried to open his mouth, gasp and close it again, all in a split second. He was quick, but Giny was quicker, and the precious rug was snatched away and held high out of reach of the frantic pup. He pranced about on his hind feet, his front feet pawing in the direction of the rug, while his excited barks sounded like the yodels of a boy whose voice is changing.

This round was over, but the battle went on. Before the first lull was reached, four of Giny's rugs had been folded and put high on a closet shelf out of his reach, and these were soon joined by three sofa pillows. Our shoes and slippers had been picked up, chewed, and carried to the far corners of the cabin. Only when he was exhausted, and we were too, did the hectic activity subside. Giny and I sank into chairs, and Zanie promptly climbed up in her lap, looked around with that "wasn't that fun" expression, then with a sigh of contentment curled up, tucked his head under her arm and went to sleep.

"What's a person going to do?" asked Giny as she looked affectionately and helplessly at the little fellow.

"I'm going to take him back by that farm house where we found him and toss him out of the car," I said. But Giny knew I wouldn't, and Zanie knew it, and I did too.

Zanie's introduction to Zipper and Zowie was delayed a few hours. Zipper came first, making her way through the brush, headed for the kitchen door. There she knew she would receive a luscious bottle of warm milk. Zanie was draped over the front step at the moment, probably dreaming of Navajo rugs, slippers and things. The fawn came into the open right before him. In an instant he was on his feet trotting toward the new creature. Zipper froze in statuelike pose, looking wild-eyed at this unexpected guest. On Zanie went, turning his head from one side to the other, the hair down his spine rising in little knots. Zipper stretched her nose far to meet him.

When they were but inches apart, Zanie emitted a sharp little bark. Zipper went right up in the air in one of her finest bronco leaps. Then she whirled and raced away through the brush. Zanie apparently thought he had frightened this larger creature half out of her speckled hide. His doggy egotism was inflated to the utmost. With a bark and a growl all mixed together, he raced away in pursuit. We could trace their route by breaking twigs and more puppy barks.

Then suddenly the sounds changed! Zanie's barks became yipes, and the cracking of twigs headed our way. Out of the brush came our pup friend very much on the defensive, racing wildly and making every effort to get his all too short tail between his legs. He ran his nose flat into the screen door and, as Giny opened this for him, he darted through the house, ending up under the bed where but a few hours before he had dragged the rug.

In the meantime Zipper put on one of her cutest bucking displays, acting as if her front feet wanted to go one way while her hind feet went another.

Zanie regained his composure sufficiently to look out the screen door at the cavorting fawn. He got the idea that four-footed jumping jack wasn't going to eat him alive after all. Zipper discovered him looking out and advanced to the door. She licked the screen directly in front of his nose. Then he licked the screen in front of her nose. Then they both licked at the same time, and the friendship was sealed.

Zipper was called to her bottle now, and Zanie settled once more on the front step. He didn't remain there long. Out of the brush came a graceful creature with red coat, a long bushy tail, pointed nose and ears, and alert, sharp eyes. Zanie rose but he didn't rush at the new creature. His experience with Zipper had cured him of that. He walked a step at a time, his muscles straining as if he were pulling a heavy load.

"Zanie," said Giny from an open window. "Zanie, that is Zowie. Be nice, now. You two are going to be the best of friends."

Zanie paused to look up at her, but he wasn't convinced about the budding friendship. At least he had something this time that was somewhere near his size.

The fox never moved a hair until Zanie was a few inches from him. Then he arched his back and tail like a frightened cat, but in place of leaping, he slowly settled to the ground, his chin resting on his forepaws, his sharp eyes glued on the pup. Zanie looked at him in bewilderment. This mild move he hadn't expected and he was completely disarmed. He sank to the ground too, and placed his chin on his forepaws. For many minutes they held their poses, perhaps carrying on communication in ways we human beings do not understand. Then they started inching toward each other, crawling on their stomachs. As their noses came within touching distance, suddenly they leaped at each other, and there followed the wildest rough-and-tumble fight. It looked and sounded serious at first, and we went out hurriedly to make sure no one was getting hurt. But it was all in fun, and there began one of the most interesting animal friendships I have witnessed.

The next day Zanie was discovering ways to pester and tease his newly made friends. He found that Zipper did not like to have her nose licked, and so on every possible occasion he licked it. Also he made the important discovery that Zowie did not like to have his tail bitten. Hence he grabbed for it every time it was within reach. Giny and I were watching out the window on one occasion when Zanie sneaked up behind the fox and took a good firm hold on his royal tail. Apparently somewhat angered, Zowie whirled around and grabbed hold of Zanie's short appendage. Growling and biting, they whirled about in sort of an animal ring-around-a-rosy until both were out of breath—and we were too.

The next day there was another trip to town for mail and supplies. This time we must get biscuit in addition to the fox food and fawn food.

"Listen, Giny," I said as we got into the car. "I don't know whether I am getting superstitious or not, but I am afraid to go to town. This whole country seems to be in a conspiracy. I feel as if there is someone behind every tree ready to poke a baby animal in my arms. Now please help me—don't let me take on any more trouble. Even if we see an orphaned white-throated sparrow or a deserted baby hummingbird with a mother to support—don't let me take them in!"

Giny laughed. "All right, I'll keep looking behind all trees to make sure there is no one waylaying you. As to those orphans, I wish you would stop worrying. I believe there is an intelligence beyond our own at work in this, and we will see a plan unfold before us."

"I'll try to share your faith," I said a bit weakly. "Please watch those trees!"

But the surprise that day had in store for us wasn't behind any trees. It was right out in the open. We had finished our shopping and were headed for home when, at the edge of town, we heard several dogs barking and some boys shouting wildly. We stopped the car and looked out in a field where the excitement was taking place. A baby skunk was running as fast as a skunk ever runs. Two boys and three dogs were running after it. I jumped from the car.

"Hey, boys," I called. "Don't hurt that little thing. He hasn't done anything to you, and he won't if you let him alone."

They paid no attention to me. "Go get him, Sport," cried one of them. "Get him, boy, get him!"

The dog raced forward, followed by the other two, all anxious to please their master. Then the skunk stopped running and calmly faced its pursuers. He chattered his teeth and beat the ground with his feet. Tiny as he was, he seemed to be warning his bloodthirsty opponents that they were running into serious trouble.

They were in no mood to take advice, however, either from the skunk or me.

Seeing the white-striped kitty at bay, the dogs came in for the kill—and ran head on into a thick, yellow mist which the little one directed with amazing accuracy. The leader dog caught the discharge full in the face, and in an instant was rolling over and over on the ground, saturated with misery. The other two mongrels had sufficient to send them racing the other way with all the enthusiasm they had shown in the chase. The boys had their handkerchiefs to their eyes and nose, while their clothes soaked up a perfume that would make them most unwelcome even in their own homes. The breeze carried record of the battle far and wide.

Unruffled and calm stood the skunk, looking as if he regretted that he had to be so severe. He wouldn't weigh a pound soaking wet, and yet he had put to flight dogs that were more than a hundred times his weight.

Then to my astonishment I saw one of the boys pick up a stone about as large as a baseball. Before I could stop him, he threw it at the retreating skunk. It struck the ground a few feet short of the animal, bounced and then hit the little creature in the shoulder. Over he rolled

and then lay very still. The boy would have thrown a second stone, except that I had reached him by that time and wrenched it from his hand.

"That's a cowardly thing to do, lad," I said reprovingly. "That little fellow has put up a good fight. At least you could be a good sport about it."

"Well, he's a pest, ain't he?" asked the boy, trying to justify himself.

"No, he is not a pest," I declared. "The skunk is a valuable animal. He destroys many things—bugs, mice and worms—that are pests. You ought to be ashamed to stone him like that, or to sick dogs on him the way you did."

The boys seemed amazed that anyone would say anything good about a skunk. They asked me many questions about the habits of the animals, as the tone of our talk became friendly and informative. Finally one of them said, "Aw, I'm sorry! I thought all a skunk did was to go around smelling bad."

I believe the boys were sorry. Much evil is but ignorance anyway. They went with me as I picked up the skunk and examined him. He was still alive, and I could not tell how badly he was hurt. "Why, he's pretty!" said one of the boys. "I never saw one close before."

We emptied a grocery box and with some rags made a bed for the injured creature. Giny held the box in her lap to protect him from bumps.

For a time we drove along in silence, then I heard a delighted laugh from Giny. "He's moving, Sam," she exclaimed. "He is coming out of it—I know he is."

Down in the box our striped friend was moving ever so slightly, but enough to show there was life.

"Move over, Zipper, Zowie and Zanie," said Giny with a chuckle. "Move over and make room for . . ." She hesitated.

"Make room for whom?" I asked.

"For Zinnia!"

VI

"PLEASED TO MEET YOU"

ZINNIA had been only stunned, struck by a glancing blow of the rock. The skunk proved to be a little female, probably about six weeks old.

Before we reached the island she was moving about her box. From among our groceries we procured a few bites of food which she accepted from our fingers. She didn't hold it against us in the least that some of our kind had abused her so severely but a short time before. Sometimes, in the important matters of forgiveness and returning good for evil, our forest brethren are more obedient than we are.

Once home, we moved Zinnia into the small, comfortable cage where many of our Sanctuary animals had known refuge. She would be kept there only until we were sure she was fully recovered and then—oh, what *would* we do with her? A skunk on the same island with a fox, a dog, a deer and subject to the regular visits of porcupines, raccoons and other animals presented a hazard, to say the least.

"You could have the odor sack removed," Giny volunteered.

"It wouldn't be fair," I protested. While the removal of the scent organ is not a severe experience, for a skunk and animals so treated obviously live on in comfort, still it had a special objection here. "We would not want her confined," I went on, it being our conviction that all animals love liberty. "And it wouldn't be fair to release her in the woods without her natural defense. We saw how she needed it today!"

The next morning when I went to examine Zinnia I was pleased to find her acting quite normally. Otherwise this was a day of frustration.

Bent on solving the mounting problem of Zipper, Zowie, Zanie and Zinnia, we drove first to the home of our good friends, Ray and Ada. We found them in a mood of great excitement. A letter had just been received from their lovely daughter, June, who was finishing her first year in college. Could they drive down and get her?

"And we are going to do it," Ray said enthusiastically. "We will be there, car all packed, the day her school closes—and away we go for a month or more. Isn't that wonderful?"

Yes, that was wonderful. We talked about their coming trip, entered their anticipated joy—and went away carrying our own problem unsolved.

Then we called on Merl, the only other friend who might be interested in our four Z's. Unknowingly he too compelled us to keep quiet on the subject of our visit. He was anticipating a happy summer. A family of life-long friends were coming to stay with him. The only drawback was that this family had two huge police dogs. "They are wonderful dogs," Merl said, "but they are not trained for the forest. It means that not a deer, porcu-pine or any other creature will get near my home this year—and I'll miss them."

So, once more we kept our problem secret and went away.

"There remains one thing to do," I began saying as we drove toward home. "I have been hesitating to suggest it——"

"You mean cancel our trip to the Grand Canyon and stay home?" interrupted Giny excitedly.

"No, no. We couldn't do that. We have many lectures booked for next winter at which we have promised a Grand Canyon film."

"Then, what?" Giny was disappointed.

"Well, we can find a home for Zanie without difficulty. There are many people who want a pup like him. Then we can have Zipper, Zowie and Zinnia taken to a game farm. They will . . ."

"Yes," broke in Giny, "they will put them in cages and make them stay there. Those little fellows that love liberty so much would be put in jail. I couldn't stand it."

"Yes, I have been going over that in my own thoughts," I went on. "I don't like it either, but what else can we do?"

Giny was silent for a moment and then she said helplessly, "I don't know."

However, if we had a problem it was certain our animals at the Sanctuary did not. Their mood of merriment was never exhausted. From morning until night they had one endless picnic, constantly inventing new stunts of play, but never forgetting the old ones. We could worry if we wanted to, they were just too busy being happy.

Time had come to introduce Zinnia to the rest of the family. She was quite well and was beginning to resent her cage. She had completely accepted Giny and me and permitted us to handle her freely. However, she was chewing at the wires of her cage and obviously seeking the outside world. We decided to liberate her. It was a tense moment when we did, for we could not be sure of what her reaction to the other animals would be, nor what they would think of her.

"Zinnia," I said to her, taking her in my hands.

"Sniff, sniff," went Zinnia, reaching her cold little nose up to mine.

"Zinnia," I said, "you are going to be free on our island today. It isn't a very big island. Giny and I can't go very far in any direction without running into the water. What I want to ask of you is that you don't use your—that is, your means of defense—your potent perfume here. The island couldn't stand it, Zinnia. It would just float away."

"Sniff, sniff." I couldn't make out whether this was a promise or not.

"There are other folks on the island besides you, Zinnia," I continued. "There is Zipper, a swell little fawn. Surely you won't be afraid of her. And there is Zanie, the crazy pup. Please don't think he is anything like those big bullies that you had to handle so roughly. And there is Zowie. He's a fox, but he isn't like foxes you might meet in the woods. He has lived here for many days and he has learned there is such a thing as friendship in the world. Please, oh, please, be patient with Zowie, Zinnia. Please!"

My concern was only because I had underrated the intelligence of Zanie. The pup came trotting up to me looking as if he knew there was new business at hand. I placed Zinnia on the ground before him. He welcomed her like an official greeter of a chamber of commerce. There could be no question that he was delighted with her, and she with him. He licked her on the nose, played with her and batted her about rather roughly with his paws. She liked her treatment, however, and followed the dog every step he took—a habit that persisted all during their days at the Sanctuary.

Now Zanie took over the job of host and introducer. He led Zinnia about until they confronted Zowie. I wondered about this meeting. His ancestors and hers have long been at enmity, and anything could happen. However, blessed little Zanie was equal to the situation. When Zowie showed a tendency to snap at the newcomer, the dog placed himself right between them. He continued this caution until the fox comprehended the fact that friendliness was the mode of the moment. Zipper came in for an introduction, and Zanie stayed right on the scene to see that everybody liked everybody.

Toward darkness we witnessed the kind of event that always raises our conception of the mental caliber of the animal world. The skunk, dog, fox and deer were feeding at the same time from a large dish of milk. It was the sort of scene that makes one wonder just how much intelligence and comradeship is hidden beneath the veneer of fear and enmity which appear on our first approach to nature. Certainly it suggests that such an expression as "natural enemies" is based upon a fallacy.

Zanie seemed especially satisfied with the day's work. He paused between lappings of milk to lick Zipper and Zinnia on their noses and then he took a playful bite at Zowie's tail.

"If those little fellows can settle their differenecs so intelligently," commented Giny as we stood looking at them, "surely it isn't too much to expect nations to do as well."

VII

DON'T TELL A SOUL!

I BEGAN my letter to the Conservation Department with such regret that it seemed every time I struck a key on the typewriter it brought down a sledge hammer on the back of my neck. "Gentlemen:" it started. "I have on hand three young animals that I would like to get rid of . . ." I snatched that letter out of the typwriter. It was dishonest. The last thing in the world I wanted to do was to get rid of those animals. I tried again. "Gentlemen: I have on my island three young animals that are giving me quite a problem." That wasn't fair either. These animals weren't giving me a problem. It wasn't their fault that I had to go to Grand Canyon. They hadn't even asked to come to our Sanctuary. I began again. "Gentlemen:"

"Sam!" cried Giny. "Sam, stop Zanie. He has one of your best slippers."

Out of the bedroom raced the pestersome pup, his eyes dancing with glee, his ears flapping in the breeze, his mouth full of my slipper. I made a grab for him, but he was too quick. He bumped the screen door open and raced out into the woods. Zowie saw him go and ran after him. I followed, and Zipper came along just for the ride.

Out under some trees I found the fox and pup working hard at changing the form of that slipper. One had hold of the toe, the other of the heel, and they were engaged in a tug of war that had already increased the length of the shoe by about four sizes. I lunged at them. Zanie let go his end, and Zowie spurted away with the prize!

Zanie ran to me, jumped up as if to say, *Whoopie, isn't this fun?*—and disappeared after the fox.

After an hour of futile searching I returned to the cabin. There stood Zanie on the step, with my slipper in his mouth. "Giny," I called, "Zanie has found my slipper and brought it back to me."

"Indeed he has *not!*" cried Giny, rushing to the door. "That is your other slipper. He just took it." And then there was another wild chase about the island, ending in my utter defeat. Two slippers were buried, hidden, or eaten alive. At least, we never found them.

"Gentlemen:" the paper in the typewriter still said. I wanted to add to it, "I'm inflicted with the most aggravating pup in the world named Zanie. I earnestly request that you take him away and imprison him for life—or longer." But they are not concerned about dogs unless they have been caught molesting wild life. So I directed the tone of the letter to its original purpose. I wrote:

It has been my pleasure to care for three young animals. There is a fawn, a fox and a skunk. It is necessary for me to spend some weeks in the Grand Canyon making a film, and during this time there will be no one at my Wisconsin home. I will be most grateful if you will take these animals to your game farm where they may have proper supervision and protection. . . .

Before the letter was finished to the point of signature, there was a knock at our back door. It proved to be one of the state wardens whom I knew as Big Ben. After Giny and I had greeted him, and we were seated in our living room, I remarked, "I was just writing your department a letter. Did you know what was to be in it, and have you come for the animals already?"

"Come for the animals?" countered Big Ben. "Heavens no, I didn't come for any animals—I came to bring you some."

Giny and I looked at each other.

"Yep," Big Ben went on. "I had to take out some beavers from a place where they were flooding a railroad with their pond. I have seven—all young. Want them?"

Seven beavers—all young! For years I had wanted just such a consignment.

"We-ell," Big Ben was saying, "what can we do with them?"

"Ben," I declared, "I can't take them. I am going away, and I just can't look after them. This is the wrong year. Bring me some beavers next spring and I'll grab at them. But not now."

Ben was sort of quiet. Presently he said, "Well, I'm sorry. But if you can't, why, you can't. Guess I'll have to put them in Heron Creek."

"Heron Creek?" I questioned.

"Yes, it'll have to be Heron Creek. That's government land, and there are aspen trees for food."

"But Heron Creek!" I persisted. "Why, that is right near . . ."

"Yes," said Big Ben, "I know what you mean. That is near Old Pete's cabin, and it is like planting a lamb alongside a wolf's den. He'll let 'em live till spring anyway. Their hides won't be worth much before that."

"But, Ben, how about Kimball Creek, or Jones Creek, or the Pine River?"

"All trout streams—not allowed to put beaver in them. Nope, they have to go in Heron Creek. I'll keep quiet about it, but Old Pete, or else Bill or Ed, will find them. They have noses like hound dogs. Oh—almost forgot—here is a special-delivery letter the postmaster asked me to bring out."

He drew a wrinkled envelope out of his pocket and handed it to me. I opened it. It was from Marge, Hi-Bub's mother. In excitement I read the first few lines, then unable to suppress myself I jumped right up in the air, letting out a war whoop that caused both Giny and Big Ben to jump.

"What in the world is the matter with you?" Giny asked.

"Ya-hoo," I yelled. "It's all right, everything is all right. Sure I want those beavers. And don't you dare try to take my animals away."

"What's eatin' you?" asked Big Ben, as excited as he ever gets.

"I tell you, everything is all right," I insisted. "I believe in Santa Claus, I believe in everything. Here, listen to this, from Hi-Bub's mother:

'Dear Friends:
As you know, Hi-Bub hasn't been himself for some time. We still do not know what it is that's bothering him.

Now it seems to be affecting his health. He isn't really ill, but seems to be nervous. You know he planned to go to summer school, but his principal has convinced him and us that he should not do this. He needs to be outdoors, up in the woods . . .' "

"Can't you read faster?" broke in Giny.

"Wait," I directed. "Listen to this:

'He needs to be outdoors, up in the woods this summer. The principal says that it will do him much more good than to study. Now Hi-Bub has renewed his friendship with Tony, whom you had north a few years ago! Tony is a wonderful boy and seems to be the only one Hi-Bub wants to be with these days. Now here is my request: Could you find a place where these two boys could work up there—most any kind of work at a resort, a boys' camp—just so they can be up there? Or, could we dare hope you would want them at your Sanctuary?' "

Giny was on her feet throwing her arms about me. "Do we know a place where they can work!" she exclaimed, almost at the point of tears. *"Do* we? Oh, I knew we would find the answer."

"We'll turn the Sanctuary over to them!" I enthused. "Both are trained in boy scouting, they can take care of themselves. Hi-Bub can cook. It's all perfect! Perfect!"

"Can you tell me what all this going on has to do with seven baby beavers?" put in Big Ben.

"Everything, Old Top!" I said. "Excuse me for not explaining. Hi-Bub and Tony are two fine boys whom we have known for years. They are wonderful with animals.

This letter opens the way for them to come north and stay while we are in the West. They can take care of our island, the beavers, the skunk and all. Ben, you couldn't possibly know what this news means to us."

"I am beginning to," said Ben, rising. "It means a lot to me. I sure didn't want to put those beavers in Heron Creek. Now, come down to earth for a minute. Where are we going to put them—in your Vanishing Lake?"

I reflected for a moment. "No," I said, "Vanishing Lake isn't so good. There are no aspens there for food—mostly birch and black spruce."

"Four Mile Creek?" questioned Ben.

"Too well known," I commented. "We lost a fine colony of beavers there to trappers. I would like to hide these animals away, if I could." I suddenly caught an idea. "Giny, do you remember one time during a hike we passed beyond the old cyclone area west of us and came onto another lake about the size of Vanishing Lake?"

Giny did.

"And I said to you at the time that it was a good spot for beavers—plenty of aspens, pin cherries and alders. I could find it again, I feel sure."

I brought forth a map of the region, and indicated the general location of the lake. "It was somewhere along this section line," I told Ben. "I am not exactly sure, but somewhere in that direction."

"And we are going to carry seven young beavers through a cyclone blow-down to a lake that is just somewhere?" questioned Ben. "Have you ever carried seven beavers in crates on such a jaunt?"

"The way I feel now I could carry most anything anywhere," I assured him. "Come on, let's get the beavers back there, so you can get my answer to that letter in tonight's mail."

Ben was right about the task before us. The beavers, though young and small, made a difficult load. They were in crates equipped with straps so they could be carried on our backs, but they were heavy and constantly shifting their weight. The task was made more tiring by the fact we didn't know just where we were going. However, we held to the survey line by compass, blazing a trail as we went, and after two hours of laborious travel we reached the lake. Here we liberated our charges.

They were cunning things, with sleek, beautiful fur, wide flat tails, little ears and shoe-button eyes that kept looking at us as if saying, *How long are you going to keep tossing us around? How about some water and a few bites of popple bark?*

"It's all out there, fellows," I said, as we began taking them from their boxes and releasing them at the edge of the lake.

Big Ben amused me in his handling of the young animals. As a professional trapper, he was expected to remedy beaver problems, to live-trap any animal that was causing damage and transfer it to a more favorable location. He was supposed to be calloused by his job. Now as he released each beaver he fondled it a bit and offered fragments of fatherly advice. "Here, number one, you are on your own now. I kinda hate to see you go, you've been so much trouble. Remember there are wolves and wild cats here—don't go far from the pond. Number two, sorry my trap scarred your nose a little. You'll be all right now. Number three, what you looking so sad about? This is a beaver heaven—or maybe you didn't want to go to heaven. Number four, you're the scrappy fellow. You better get over it now. You eggs have to stick together." And numbers five, six and seven were also sent into the water with his blessing. They were soon swimming about, their heads popping up in various parts of the lake.

"They will be all right here," said Ben, looking after them. "You'll be surprised at what they do to this lake. They will clean out the springs and put a dam over the outlet. The water will rise, and it will be cleaner too when they get to work." He felled several aspen trees near the water's edge. "That will give them food until they get their bearings and do their own cuttings."

We followed our blazed trail back to our own lake. Giny had supper ready for us, and we sat talking about our beavers. "Sure glad it worked out this way," Big Ben said. "They might fight among themselves. That's a lot of beavers to have in one place. On the other hand, they may widen that lake out until there is room for them all. Hope they will."

Big Ben filled out his report on the planting of the beavers, while I typed a hurried reply to Marge's letter. "We not only want Tony and Hi-Bub at the Sanctuary for the entire summer—we need them urgently!" I wrote, briefly summarizing our situation.

"Say," Big Ben demanded as I handed him my letter to mail. "I have to tell where I planted those seven. Has the lake got a name?"

"No, it hasn't. It's just a plain woods lake, I guess."

"Well, if it hasn't a name, we better give it one. Suppose I put down here 'planted in *Somewhere Lake!*'"

"*Somewhere Lake* it is. That sounds good," commented Giny.

"And outside of this report, I think we'd better let those little fellows be a secret," said Ben. "You folks and I have seven secrets just between ourselves."

"Seven secrets," repeated Giny, her thought distant. "The Seven Secrets of Somewhere Lake."

VIII

THE BEST OF FRIENDS

ZANIE was taken into our confidence about the Seven Secrets of Somewhere Lake. One trip over the blazed trail and he knew the way perfectly. Two trips, and this was established as one of his favorite adventures. All we had to do was whisper, "Zanie, we're going to Somewhere Lake," and he looked like a collection of animated dynamite. He was quickly taught not to bark when this was our destination, though. Oh, dear no, this was a secret! So when we asked him if he wanted to go to Somewhere Lake, he expressed his enthusiasm in violent wiggles, wild jumping, and dancing eyes, but his only vocal comments were some breathy *woofs* that you couldn't hear across the room.

The Seven Secrets studied us as closely as we did them. They were wary when we appeared along the shores of Somewhere Lake, yet their reactions were tempered by curiosity if not an actual tinge of friendliness. They had felt the touch of human hands and taken food from our fingers when they were released. Their wild instincts led them to slap the water and dive when they saw us, but before many minutes we would see them come cautiously to the surface and look us over carefully.

The spot on the shore where they had first been liberated we designated as a good-will feeding station, and each time we came we put out a supply of apple slices, carrots and other tasty tidbits. They were taking our offerings, but not while we were present. We found their tracks at the spot, and always the food was gone. We felt that we had reason to hope for an intimate relationship.

The season in which the seven had been liberated is vacation time for beavers. The little engineer of the wilds truly is the hard-working creature he is reputed to be. But he is not a fanatic about it. When autumn days are upon him and he knows winter is just around some corner, he gets down to business and lets the chips fall where they may. He cuts down trees and cuts them up, to obtain bark and leaves for food and logs for his dams and houses. But when the winter challenge has been met and spring comes again with its abundant new growth and easy living conditions, the beaver lets up on his labor. He lolls in the sunshine, he plays about his pond, he rears his youngsters, and he may even go on a vacation trip many miles into the surrounding forest.

Our beavers cut but two trees in the first week they were in their new home. These were aspens that stood near the water, and obviously this cutting was only for food, for while they had been nibbling at the leaves and bark, the trees had not been cut into lengths for handling. We found a number of indistinct trails they were using in exploring the land about the lake. It was certain that they were getting well acquainted with their new home, and everything we saw indicated that they were satisfied.

If we were slow in making buddies of the beavers, Zanie was not. One morning we saw him bridge the gap between his world and theirs.

When we arrived at the lake we could see dimly the forms of two beavers at the feeding station. Nothing had been left out for them the night before, and they appeared to be searching. We halted back of some bushes and studied them through binoculars. Zanie was conscious of their presence and became wildly excited. He whined a bit, ripples of tension sweeping over his body.

"Quiet, boy," I whispered to him.

However, despite my protests, he advanced out into the open, going directly toward the two flattails. His pace was steady though not in the least hurried. The beavers discovered him and turned quickly as if to flee into the water. But they did not go, and why I cannot say. Here was a creature new to them, and it seemed logical they would seek the safety of their pond until they had absolute assurance. While the beaver is a fierce fighter when he is cornered, having been known to dispose of the wildcat in combat, his main defense is in his ability to disappear into his pond and to remain submerged. Some influence prevented the animals from fleeing that morning. What that *something* is I do not know even yet, though we saw it manifested often in Zanie's experiences with other animals. Did the very manner of the dog assure the beavers? Was there a peculiar scent reaching their nostrils that told them they had nothing to fear? Was it a finely developed instinct closely akin to intuition? Whatever the *something,* we saw convincing evidence of its presence and potency that day.

The beavers stopped and faced the dog. He continued slowly, resolutely, each step being a variety of a point.

As he got close the waiting animals showed a little nervousness, but they did not run. Then came the great s-t-r-e-t-c-h, which we had observed when Zanie met Zowie and Zipper. His hind feet held to a chosen spot, and his front feet walked on. He reached and reached toward the foremost of the beavers, and the flattail reached for him. At last their noses touched! Is it in Africa that the form of caress among primitive people is the rubbing of noses? Well, that is the kiss of the animal world too. Zanie's stubby tail began wagging violently. The beavers rose on their hind legs to look him over more thoroughly. Zanie gave several happy little barks and pranced back and forth. Then he whirled about and raced back to us, his joy unbounded.

"Nice work," I praised him. "You made some friends, didn't you, Old Top? I wish I had your skill."

Zanie took our praise and petting as a well-deserved reward, and then he raced back to his new pals. His approach was too rapid this time, and they retreated into the water. Zanie stood at the edge of the lake looking frustrated. Then he discovered one of the beavers that had surfaced fifty feet out. In he went, determined to have a romp with these interesting creatures.

Zanie is a fine water dog, but he was out of his class that day. He made straight for the beaver, giving his muffled barks. The flattail waited for him to draw near, then slapped the water and made a crash dive, splashing Zanie's face. Zanie circled all around looking for the animal. Now word seemed to spread among the beavers that they had a stooge at hand, and they made the most of

it. Beaver heads began appearing at various places on the pond. Zanie nearly went mad. He swam at one beaver after another, always getting just close enough to get a good shower bath as the animals whacked the water with their tails and dived. They tormented the breath out of him. He became so excited he forgot his pledge of secrecy and let out several sharp barks—and who wouldn't with all seven of these Secrets picking on you that way?

At last he climbed out on the mossy shore and barked his challenge to any and all of them. We reminded him of his duty to be quiet, and immediately he muffled his voice. The beavers continued their slapping and diving about the lake. Obviously they were having a good time, and even though he was the victim, Zanie was having one too.

A letter came from Hi-Bub. It was quiet and reserved in tone, but the big fact was that he and Tony were coming. The date of their arrival was so near at hand that Giny and I were sent into a flurry of activity to get ready for them. The closing sentence of Hi-Bub's letter I read over and over again. "I guess you know," he wrote, "that I would rather be at your Sanctuary than anywhere else in the world."

IX

TWO BOYS AND A PIE

Dɪᴅ ʏᴏᴜ ever notice that a railroad engine puffs differently when it has on the train someone you especially love? It seems to me it does. Of course the new modern Diesel engines just come into the station without much change in expression, but the real, old-time, huffing, puffing, cinder-blowing steam engine always makes a lot of fuss when delivering someone you are anxious to see.

We still have steam engines on our little branch-line railroad. I have heard that we are not important enough to rate a Diesel, and also that our track is not strong enough to support one. Whatever it is that keeps our old-fashioned huffer and puffer in service, I am grateful for it.

The engine was nearly on time that morning when our two boys arrived, something very unusual in itself. Its heavy puffs seemed to say, "I got 'em, I got 'em, I got 'em," and when it had accomplished its stop, it stood there drawing in deep breaths to compensate for its extra exertion.

The Pullman porter recognized me as he stepped off the train. "I have a couple of mighty fine boys for you this morning, Mister Campbell," he said with a smile that had made him famous and well liked on this line.

"Hello, Hi-Bub!" cried Giny, discovering our two

boys back of the baggage on the car platform. "Hello, Tony!" We waved and called our greetings back and forth while the porter unloaded the suitcases.

I kept staring at the two lads. It was hard to believe these were the boys we had known at our Sanctuary in years gone by. Hi-Bub had grown even since I had seen him in the winter, though he looked thin about his face. Perhaps it was my own attitude in the matter that made me think so, but it seemed to me he was already beginning to look as stoical as an adding machine and methodical as a file case.

Tony was shooting up like a bean stalk. He was destined to be tall and slender. To be so fitted his manner and the look in his eyes. There was an exquisite gentleness about the lad that was in no way weakness. His handshake was firm, his manner easy and graceful, his bearing strong, but you felt that he would never knowingly harm any living thing.

It was home-coming at our island that day. The first one to greet the two boys was, of course, Zanie. The bombastic pup acted as if he had known them all his life. He jumped upon them, he licked their faces, he chewed their ankles, he raced in circles about them and finally took Tony's cap and hid it in the brush.

Anyone disbelieving in love at first sight would have been healed of his skepticism while watching the meeting of Tony and Zanie. Tony looked down at the wiggling creature at his feet saying, mostly to himself, "No! No, I don't believe it. There couldn't be such a pup." He stooped down and took Zanie in his arms, and the dog was so uncontrollably happy he howled. It was like the reunion of two long-separated brothers, and we saw here the beginning of a companionship which deepened each day that followed.

In the meantime we heard a call that Hi-Bub and Tony recognized at once. "Honk, honk, honk" came from high in a white pine. "Is it Salt?" asked Hi-Bub, with a flash of his old enthusiasm. "Come down here, you old rascal, and stick a quill in me for old times' sake."

Salt was coming down, followed by Pepper, both honking happily. When they reached the ground the two boys picked them up by the forelegs and swung them high overhead.

"You remember how to do it, don't you?" asked Giny.

"I've done this a thousand times in my dreams," Hi-Bub was saying, now holding Salt across his forearm. "Salt looks the same as he always did. I believe he hasn't grown since I last saw him."

"Probably has reached his maximum," I remarked. "He is a wonderful animal, never forgetting us. I have no doubt some of his grunts have been, 'Where are Hi-Bub and Tony?'"

"Oh, oh—here come the chipmunks," said Tony, putting Pepper down and getting ready for the next customer.

I supplied the boys with some peanuts, and soon the little animals were jumping to their hands, climbing up their trouser legs, dodging in and out of pockets, and sitting on their shoulders or heads. Several of our friendly chickadees joined the growing circle, snatching peanut crumbs from the boys' hands. Cheer, the red-winged blackbird, came to see what all the excitement was about. Blue jays and red squirrels arrived.

I studied Tony and Hi-Bub as they responded to this wild and exciting welcome. Tony's face beamed, and, though he was never a talkative person, his expressive eyes said the things his tongue did not. Each creature that came to him was received with an unmistakable love.

Hi-Bub too was responding to the friendly approaches of these animal friends. There was a tenderness in his handling of the creatures that was closely akin to reverence. But even now there persisted in his eyes a look of sadness. His laugh died out almost before it began, and his smile barely moved the corners of his mouth. He gave me the impression of someone who was carrying a burden of such weight that it overshadowed everything else life could offer. I was glad when Tony dropped a couple of peanuts in the open collar of Hi-Bub's shirt. In went a chipmunk after the peanuts, and in went a red squirrel after the chipmunk. Hi-Bub could not be stoical now. He let out a yell as the two animals raced about against his bare skin, tickling and scratching him. "Yow!" he yelled. "Go hold your battle someplace else. I'm neutral." But the two creatures continued to scuffle about his waistline until he unbuttoned his shirt and set them free.

"Tony," he said to his friend, who was leaning against a tree, his eyes rolled up to the sky in pretended innocence, "I'm going to do that same thing to you—only it will be skunks I use, so help me!"

"Speaking of skunks," said Tony with forced calmness, "have you looked back of you lately? Don't step if you value your life, don't step any other direction, and don't stay where you are."

Hi-Bub looked cautiously around under these bewildering instructions. There, not six feet from him, he saw a skunk eying him curiously. Hi-Bub started to take a step. Up went the skunk's tail, and Hi-Bub stopped, one foot held in the air. His face was a study, a mixture of amusement, concern and wonder. Tony slipped behind a tree and then peeked around to see what was going to happen. Giny and I were shaking with suppressed laughter. This was the moment we had been waiting for, when Hi-Bub met Zinnia. It was far better than we had hoped. Hi-Bub was taken completely by surprise, and Zinnia was playing her part perfectly. He was convinced he was in company with a wild polecat and that any wrong move of his would bring disaster to the community. "Oh-h-h-h," he groaned between parted lips. "These are my best clothes. Listen, little skunky-unky, I'm not going to hurt you. I love skunks, I do."

Losing his balance, he brought his suspended foot down a little faster than Zinnia liked, and she began violently chattering her teeth and pounding the ground with her front feet.

"Why doesn't someone tell me what to do?" the boy pleaded between ventriloquist lips.

"You're doing all right," said Tony softly from behind his tree. "Just be nice to the little kitty. If anything happens we'll take care of you. We'll bury you—head down!"

Zanie broke the tension of the scene. His coming gave Hi-Bub an additional fright, for the pup made a run for

Zinnia. "You," yelled Hi-Bub. "Don't do that, Zanie, don't do that." But Zanie never hesitated. Apparently he had been looking for Zinnia, and now with his usual delight he rammed right into her, sending her rolling over

and over on the ground. Hi-Bub broke and ran, taking cover behind the same tree with Tony. There was a scuffle as each one tried to force the other out in the line of supposed danger, then they looked back, one head on each side of the tree. It was a different scene from the one they anticipated, however. In place of finding a dog in most miserable circumstances and the countryside in need of deodorant, they saw Giny holding the skunk and petting it.

"No!" exclaimed Tony. "Mrs. Campbell, you're not doing what you're doing. You couldn't be!"

"Yes, I am doing this." Giny laughed. "What is the matter with you boys getting all upset about our pet? Come here, I want you to meet Zinnia."

"You want us to meet which?"

"Zinnia. Come on—she is one of the nicest skunks in the forest."

The boys came forward cautiously, shooting many a side glance at me. "Come on, fellows," I said, leading them up to Giny and her pet. "This little one is all right. Go ahead and pet her; she loves it." Soon there was a circle about the skunk, everyone making over the creature, while Zanie tried his best to divert some attention to himself.

Within an hour our lads had met Zowie and Zipper and fallen in love with both. They moved into the same sleeping cabin they had occupied years before. Here they unpacked, got into some north-woods clothes and made ready to assume their duties at the Sanctuary.

Presently Giny announced dinner. She remembered well the tastes of these boys and planned the meal accordingly. The crowning feature was a huge blueberry pie. It was always a favorite with them.

"Listen here, young fellow," Tony said to Hi-Bub as he was finishing his second helping. "If you are going to be cook at this camp, you have to know how to bake a blueberry pie."

"I can make one," insisted Hi-Bub.

"Like this?"

"Well, I wouldn't want to be a copycat."

The boys' eyes grew heavy soon after dinner. The long day of travel, the cool air, the quiet of the forest had their heads nodding before the evening was half done. We had talked of many things, principally our plans for the Grand Canyon trip. Hi-Bub was especially stirred by the thought of mountain-lion pictures. We promised to make extra pictures for him if the opportunity came. We told of the Seven Secrets of Somewhere Lake and the hope we held for them. Then when they could listen no more, we excused them for the night.

I passed by the window of their cabin as the two boys were crawling in bed. Zanie had already assigned himself to Tony's cot, and was made quite welcome.

"M-m-m-m," I heard Tony's voice. "Isn't it hard to believe we are up here?"

"I guess it is hard for me to know what to believe," answered Hi-Bub.

X

HEART TO HEART

HI-BUB and Tony, filled with the desire to do everything just right, showered us with questions. "What will we feed Zipper? Where does Zowie sleep? Should we give Zinnia a bath?" What, where, why, when came at us constantly, and every question had to be answered. There must be fox biscuit for Zowie, milk and Pablum for Zipper, dog food for Zanie and anything and everything for Zinnia. There must be wild-bird feed at the different feeders, cracked corn for our squirrels and chipmunks, whole-wheat bread for Salt and Pepper when they came, and something put out each night for the raccoons. It wasn't enough to supply the animals with food; the boys must be present much of the time when they were eating, for the main responsibility our lads carried was to keep the animals accustomed to the presence of human beings. They must guard against hawks, owls, eagles and other predators which might attack our island creatures.

"It is no soft job you have taken on, boys," I assured them. "You will be busy day and night."

"Who cares?" sputtered Tony. "If we have to be up day and night we will just see so much more of all this— eh, Hi-Bub?"

Hi-Bub smiled and nodded his approval. "But we

84

have been here twenty-four hours," he said, "and we haven't seen those beavers yet."

"I have been saving that," I answered. "Tomorrow morning at dawn we will go to Somewhere Lake. There you will learn about the most exacting part of your work."

Dawn is a magic hour in the forest. Small wonder that primitive people as well as poets have pictured the woods filled with little folk that flee at the coming of daylight. Mystery haunts the shadows. There is a song in the tiny dew drops that cling to the ends of pine needles, a hush in the aisles as though the whole forest were listening. The distances, obscure in misty shadows, seem infinite.

The beauty of dawn was at its height the morning we went to Somewhere Lake. The two boys, Giny and I all went—and, of course, Zanie. We saw three deer that morning, lovely graceful creatures that looked more beautiful than ever in the pale light.

"So that is Somewhere Lake," Tony said softly, as we emerged from the forest and looked out on the small body of water. "Now, bring on your Secrets."

"I see one," I whispered, pointing to a beaver swimming near the far shore. The animal was towing a small branch of aspen.

"There's another," said Hi-Bub, permitting himself to get excited.

"And another, and another, and another," Giny added as several beaver heads appeared.

"*Woof*," went Zanie, in his best whisper bark.

Likely the whole seven were there, though we did not see them all at once. They kept diving and coming to the surface so it was impossible to count them accurately. While we stood watching them I cautioned the boys to guard well the secret.

"Isn't this on your land?" asked Tony, as I revealed to the boys the danger that these animals might be trapped.

"No, we are beyond our lines."

"And beyond the refuge too?"

"Yes, this territory is restricted only by seasonal hunting and trapping laws."

The boys looked seriously concerned.

"How would trappers get them?" asked Tony.

"They would do it in the wintertime with steel traps," I replied. "Have you boys ever seen a steel trap? Or an animal caught in one?"

They had not. While they looked out at the beavers swimming about in happy freedom, I told them something of the barbaric cruelty of steel trapping. It was not my desire to dwell on gruesome things and I disliked to torture the thoughts of these two fine lads who would never be cruel to anything or anyone. But the world will never correct such evils by being ignorant of their existence or indifferent to them. I told them of the fierce and merciless steel jaws that were hidden about the forest. "When an animal touches the trigger," I explained, "the trap snaps shut, usually catching the creature by one or two legs. The steel teeth sink right into the flesh or even into the bone."

Hi-Bub winced. "Does it kill the animal?" he questioned.

"No. As a rule the trapped creature is held there,

perhaps for days. Sometimes he breaks off his leg by his continual struggle, sometimes he chews it off."

"Couldn't there be a law that would stop such cruel trapping?" asked Hi-Bub, shocked at what he had heard.

"No, Hi-Bub," I replied. "At least, not yet. Laws are good only if they can be enforced and if they are voluntarily obeyed. It would take an army to enforce such a law, and few trappers have sufficient humane feeling that they would want to obey. Our only hope lies in finding some substitute way of trapping that will end this torture. Every year hundreds of thousands of traps are used in our country, and millions of animals suffer indescribably. We want to save our seven beaver friends, if we can."

"How can people do things like that?" Hi-Bub said.

"No man could do it if he knew animals as you and I do," I replied.

Tony and Hi-Bub vowed that no one would ever learn of the Seven Secrets from them.

Our conversation turned to the scene of life before us. On the far shore we could see dimly one of the Secrets feeding on the leaves of a fallen aspen. Another returned from some mission back into the woods and silently slipped into the water. Giny put some apples in an accustomed place. It seemed that her act must surely be unobserved, but within a few minutes two beavers emerged and began eating the delicacy.

"Your work is to develop the confidence of the beavers," I said to the boys. "We don't want them to be pets, but we do want them to accept us, to let us watch them at their work. If we can get them safely through the next spring and make them accept us as companions, we will look upon marvelous work at this lake."

Already there was a difference in the water of the lake. It was clearing, the brown color leaving it. Giny was astonished at the change. "When we brought them here the lake was brown as root beer," she exclaimed.

"But just how could they affect the water?" asked Tony. "They can't filter it."

"They are opening up the natural springs," I explained. "This is a spring-fed lake. But the springs have been covered over and plugged by the decayed vegetable matter washed in from the forest floor, the leaves dropped by trees, and weeds growing on the lake bottom. The flow of clear water has been hampered, and the brown of decaying vegetable matter has colored the water. Now they have discovered those springs. They dive down and pull away the debris and encourage the pure water to flow." I glanced quickly at Hi-Bub. "Sometimes such things happen in our minds," I went on, looking away. "We permit wrong thinking to clog up our lives. When this happens we have to work like beavers to clear away the things that darken thought, and let the fountains of pure inspiration flow freely once more." I dared not look at Hi-Bub now, but I felt him looking at me.

The last day before we departed for the West found our boys well prepared for the work before them. There was a car at their disposal so they could obtain supplies and mail from town, and each was licensed to drive it. They were comfortably settled in their cabin. They were to keep records of their experiences with animals and to send us regular reports about them. Already they had formed close friendships with Zipper, Zowie, Zanie and Zinnia.

"I like 'em all," said Tony, "but Zanie is my favorite."

"I'll take Zowie," chimed in Hi-Bub.

"That leaves Zipper for me," said Giny.

"And Zinnia is mine," I declared. "Any of you want to start something?"

During the last evening we sat about a campfire. It was one of those times when the world is particularly harmonious. The fire sent shadows dancing up the stately trunks of red pines, and stars appeared so low they looked to be entwined in the massed foliage overhead. The crackling of the fire echoed back and forth on the silent shores. The waters of the lake were like polished marble. In the west a sliver of a new moon crept slowly down to the horizon, closely followed by a brilliant Mars. Tony had been quoting bits of poetry suitable to the occasion— some of it his own. Zanie came into the circle, gave each one of us a lick, and then curled up near the fire.

Only Hi-Bub walked nervously about, now stooping to pet Zanie, now standing with his back to the fire looking out over the marble-surfaced lake. I watched him for a few moments and then surprised myself by saying, "Hi-Bub, Old Top, suppose you and I go canoeing? I have a hunch that up Four Mile Creek there might be a bear, a deer, a sea serpent, or something equally adventurous. Of course, if you two want to give up your poetry and come along, you are welcome," I added, looking at Giny and Tony.

"No, thanks," said Giny. "We'll keep the home fires burning."

Hi-Bub and I shoved off in our canoe. As we paddled across the lake, I looked back time and again at the red bubble of light the fire made in the midst of this immense blackness. I never cease to marvel that the sight of a campfire at night charms me now even as it did along the rivers of Indiana and Illinois when I was a boy. Repetition only increases its charm and meaning. The scene speaks in language more forceful than words of primitive sincerity, of wild beauty and natural freedom, of pure simple friendship and love. Hi-Bub looked back too, and while I couldn't see his face in the dark, I felt he was deeply affected.

At the far shore of the lake we heard a deer walking along slowly in the shallow waters. "Let's get close to him," I whispered. "Do you remember how to do it, lad?" Hi-Bub answered by action. He began sculling with his paddle submerged in a way I had taught him years ago. Our canoe moved in perfect silence as I directed it to the place from which the sounds came. Presently we were close enough to make out a graceful, shadowy form at the shore line. It was a young doe, looking like some ethereal creature in the dim light of stars and moon. Back in the woods we could hear the breaking of twigs, doubtless from a companion deer. Our deer had not noticed us yet; she was too concerned with nibbling lily pads that were floating on the shallow water, and leaves from overhanging trees.

Hi-Bub remembered the trick well. He was every inch a natural woodsman. While the deer reached for a bite he stroked silently with his paddle, but as the creature looked up, he held whatever position he was in. Closer and closer we drifted. Had the creature on the lake shore been alone, I believe we could have come close enough to touch her with the paddle, but the one back in the utter darkness of the shore-line forest gave a shrill whistling snort—the alarm note of the deer. The head, ears and white tail of the one before us shot up all at once, and the startled creature left the water with a magnificent leap that landed her deep in the shadows.

Hi-Bub let out a gasp of joy. "Wonderful, isn't it, lad?" I said to him. "An amazing thing about nature adventures is that they never wear out, they never grow old."

Hi-Bub turned slightly in the canoe. "What was that you said?" he asked. "I mean that last part, what was it?"

"Nature adventures never grow old, never wear out," I repeated, and then I added, "I think that's because they are fundamental and real."

We paddled on in silence for several minutes. Night hawks circled overhead uttering their monotone cries; bull frogs spoke out from the darkness. We were approaching the mouth of Four Mile Creek and could see the silhouettes of spruce trees reaching up into the sky.

"Hi-Bub," I said softly.

"Yes."

"The waters of your lake are muddy, Old Top. They aren't clear and sparkling the way they used to be. Your parents are worried about you, and . . . Giny and I are concerned. You know that, don't you?"

He finally got a little *yes* out.

"Sure you do. Some way you have let a lot of refuse wash in and it has covered over the springs. Don't you think it is about time to clean them out?"

Hi-Bub paddled hard for a few strokes. At last he found his voice sufficiently to say, "It would be a pretty hard job, I'm afraid."

"What of it?" I said, laughing to ease the tension. "Don't you suppose the Seven Secrets had a tough time on the bottom of that lake? They found sticks, logs and muck in their way, but they twisted and tugged and pulled things around with all their strength, and you see the results are showing up already."

A discouraging silence followed. I made one more try. "Of course, I realize it is really none of my business. . . ."

That did it!

"Oh, but it is your business," Hi-Bub broke in. "I want to be your business."

I laughed. "Well, then, you are my business. Talk things out with me, if it will help."

"Well . . ." He laid down his paddle and looked ahead. I sculled the canoe along waiting for him to collect his thoughts. "Well . . ." He began again. "I guess it is all just one thing—war."

"War!" I exclaimed.

"You may forget," he was saying, now talking freely, "that I am a junior at high school. Less than two years and I shall graduate—and they give me a diploma in one hand and a gun in the other."

I had expected his trouble to be school problems, perhaps a youthful romance that was not going so well—but not war!

"That is what the fellows keep saying—a diploma in one hand and a gun in the other. Then I am supposed to go out and fight with and kill someone called an enemy— a boy that is right now like myself. He doesn't hate me and I don't hate him—but we have to kill each other. I don't want to fight, I don't want to hurt anything. You—

you taught me that, Sam Campbell." There was almost an accusation in his voice.

I paddled on, thinking hard. It was clear to me now, very clear. Hi-Bub was building a wall about himself, a psychological defense. He was hardening himself to keep from being hurt too deeply.

"I just don't understand it," he was saying. "Our enemies in the last war are our friends now. They are the same people, though. We don't hate them any more and I guess they don't hate us. Now someone else has to be taught that he is an enemy, and we have to learn to hate him. What does it? It almost seems like that entertainment we had at school. A man showed us something about hynotism. Some boys and girls went up on the stage—just boys and girls like all the rest. But the man first made them laugh like idiots and then he made them cry, and then he made them dig ditches right on the stage. Pretty soon he brought them out of it, and they were the same boys and girls they had been. Isn't it just like that with war? Doesn't something sort of hypnotize people to make one nation hate another and make them fight? Then when it is over we see how foolish it was—until something hypnotizes us again?"

We were following the winding course of Four Mile Creek now. A muskrat swam ahead of us leaving a V-shaped wake. A great barred owl was calling from the top of a white-pine stub.

"I cannot justify war, Hi-Bub," I finally managed to say. "I only know that at times it is the lesser of two evils—the loss of freedom being the greater. Some day the world will see the error of it as clearly as you have, see that all aggression, hatred, fighting is a kind of hypnotism as you say. Then the world will resist these things."

"That is what I mean," Hi-Bub broke in. "Why don't we fight the thing that causes the trouble and not one another? Why don't we fight hatred and . . ."

". . . And fear, selfishness, greed—all the things that destroy human happiness?" I carried on his thought. "You are right, Old Top, that is the real conflict. Those are the enemies that hypnotize us when we are not on guard and make us do foolish things that are not natural to us at all. They make great nations do crazy things too."

"Yeah." Hi-Bub even laughed a little. "They go nuts, like those kids on the stage."

"And when a nation does that sort of thing, the rest of the world has to hold it back so it doesn't destroy all human happiness and freedom." I held to the opening in his thought. "But, Hi-Bub, that is only battling the results of wrong thinking. It is the thinking that needs to be handled—right in you and in me. Love, faith, kindness—those are the weapons we must use."

We were well up Four Mile Creek now, the black waters of which looked like a velvet ribbon entwined in the forest. The stream narrowed down so that both banks were nearly within paddle's length of the canoe. The course twisted and turned, making us give more attention to our paddling. We were approaching the limit of navigation, a place where a huge tree had fallen across the stream. Here the waters murmured and sang as they found their way through branches and under the large log.

"Listen, Hi-Bub," I said in a half whisper.

Hi-Bub was silent for a brief moment, then picked up his thought: "The fellows keep telling me nature is bunk. They laugh when I talk of being kind. They keep saying what fun it is to hunt. If men hunt one another, why shouldn't they hunt animals? They try to get tough as they can, and—and they laugh at me."

"Hi-Bub," I said strongly, "I *do* hear voices . . . voices you know. Listen!"

Now the lad gave his attention to the woods. A big old bull frog gave his raucous call not six feet from the canoe. Nighthawks were circling overhead. Deep in the gloom a white-throated sparrow gave one clear, high-pitched song. The murmuring of waters joined the voices of insects to complete one grand choral effect.

"Hear it, lad?" I whispered. "Forget about the city and forget what the fellows tell you. Just listen."

More and more dominating became the calls of nature. The voices of the waters reached the proportions of a chorus. There was singing, laughter, merriment as by a group of happy campers.

"You know that call, Hi-Bub," I whispered. "You and I heard it together in this very creek before, we heard it on Sanctuary Lake in Canada, we heard it in our camps when the wind was playing in the pines and waves were breaking on the shores. Do you know what I mean?"

"Yes!" responded Hi-Bub. "I hear it! The voices of the woods! Why, I had forgotten about that. Why didn't I hear it at first?"

"Just listen now," I replied. "Maybe we can answer that question later."

We sat long giving our undivided attention to that phenomenon of forest sounds which woodsmen have called the "voices of the woods." It is mysterious, but not a mystery. It is composed of the simple voices of nature, those things that are just beyond direct attention. Indians have listened to it through the ages and thought it the vocalizing of spiritual beings; nature lovers have found in it one of the most charming aspects of the woodland. Not always can we hear it. One must be absolutely quiet and receptive or the delicate and delightful effect is lost to one. It is the crowning grandeur of wild, primitive beauty.

"You've been sort of hypnotized, Hi-Bub. You were thinking more of what the world had been telling you than you were about nature. And so you have been doing things not natural to you," I said seriously. "The good things of the world are like the voices of the woods. They are quiet, calm—once likened to *a still small voice*. We have to make ourselves listen for them and to them. It seems that the other kind of things make all the noise, do all the talking. If we don't watch out that is all we hear—war, meanness, drunkenness and the like. But if we hold to what we know and don't listen to all the suggestions, we can always hear the real things and be happy in them."

We put our canoe about and slowly made our way back to the lake and the island. Tony and Giny were still reading poetry by the light of the campfire.

When at last we returned to our cabins, I walked along

with my arm about Hi-Bub's shoulders. His face wore a real smile—much like his old-time one.

"Sam Campbell," he said, "I believe we cleaned out some of my springs tonight, like the beavers do in their pond. The water looks clearer already."

XI

CANYONS AND CHIPMUNKS

"Ye crags and peaks, I'm with you once again! O sacred forms, how proud you look! How high you lift your heads into the sky! How huge you are! How mighty and how free!" Giny softly whispered these words of James Sheridan Knowles as we looked upon the awesome spectacle of the Grand Canyon.

It was early evening and we had just arrived at the north rim. A sunset of surpassing splendor reigned in the western sky. Ponderous cumulus clouds looking like gigantic sea lions rested quietly at the horizon, while the sunrays played a color symphony on their wrinkled, woolly sides. Far, far below us lay the immense, silent canyon, the hues of the sunset reflected by its mystic mountain peaks and somber cliffs. Our first evening at the Grand Canyon closed in glory that was well nigh too much for human thought to comprehend.

The park ranger gave a long whistle that curved downward at the end. "You certainly have ambitions," he commented on a request Giny and I had just made. "You want animal pictures and lots of them, and you want especially a white-tailed squirrel and a mountain lion and cub!" He sat back and looked at me thoughtfully. "Haven't we met before?" he questioned.

"It seems to me we have," I agreed. "That whistle of

yours sounded familiar. I have heard and seen you give it before, someplace."

"It is a habit," he replied, "and now I am remembering. You heard that whistle at Yellowstone National Park, for the same reason you heard it here. I was stationed there when you came and asked help in photographing grizzly bear and mountain sheep. You wouldn't ask for black bear. I could have led you to plenty of those. No, you wanted grizzly—and that is when I whistled."

I laughed. "I recall it all now. You told me where the grizzlies were and then advised me not to go there."

"And you went anyway," he carried on. "Did you get your pictures?"

"Yes, I did—and enjoyed the whole experience."

"And now you want a white-tailed squirrel and a mountain lion. Mind if I whistle again?" He did.

"Well, you picked out a job," he commented. "About two months ago I found a white-tail and made this shot."

Reaching in his desk drawer he brought forth an enlargement and placed it before Giny and me. It was an excellent picture of the white-tailed or Kaibab squirrel. In size, make up, habit and every appearance, except color, he resembles the gray squirrel of the Middle West. When seen in the tree shadows, his tail looks pure white and his body jet black, but when examined closely the tail is rather gray and the body a real dark brown. Nowhere else in the world is this strangely marked creature found. Just why he has evolved this color pattern we cannot know, but it has been suggested that it affords him winter protection. When the country is covered with snow and his predatory enemies are active, his white tail curled over his back makes him blend with the white landscape. On the other hand, it may be just his effort to be original. At any rate, he seems quite proud of his plumelike tail and keeps waving it before the world.

"It took me days to get that shot," the ranger explained. "And I haven't seen one of the squirrels since. I'll show you the area where I found him and you can search it to your heart's content. I can't give you much hope. But now, about this mountain lion . . ."

He gave another whistle. "They are around here, all right. We see their tracks fairly often, but seldom one of them. Afraid of a cougar?" he asked Giny.

"No, I'm not," she replied. "I like cats of any size."

"There is no need to be afraid," he assured her. "I wouldn't want to get one cornered, for he can put up a terrific fight. But I have never known one to make a deliberate attack on a human being. They always run away. That is the trouble. As soon as you get in the same country with one, he is gone, so swiftly and silently you never would know he was around if you did not find his tracks. But to find one in position to make pictures, and especially one with a cub . . ."

I gave the whistle this time. "Thought I would save you the breath," I said.

We spread before us maps of the region and discussed the areas in which cougar were still known to be. We talked with guides who were making frequent trips into the Canyon, hunters, trappers and wardens who had traveled far along the outer margins of the National Park. From each came the same story. They had seen evidences of cougar, but not the animals themselves.

I was pleased to note in all these men a more tolerant attitude toward the mountain lion than formerly prevailed. Until recent years all through the West there was a determination to exterminate the creature. He was listed as a wanton killer that must be destroyed. Now it was seen that this great cat is an important element in the balance of nature. Truly, he is entirely a predator. His major food is deer. However, if there are no factors to keep the numbers of deer down, overpopulation results with some sad consequences. There has been no sharper lesson in this than in the Kaibab. For years efforts were made to exterminate the cougar and other predators. High bounties were paid on them. The deer herd reached such proportions that there was starvation, and some varieties of trees were threatened with extinction by the frantic feeding of the animals. Now the place of the big cat in the wild-life scheme was better understood.

By the time we had finished our talks with various advisers, our day was done. We had many plans, none of which offered much hope of finding mountain lions. "There is a fire lane leading into those wilder areas northwest," our ranger said in summary. "It is difficult driving, and I cannot promise what it will do to your car. That is your best country. Better camp there and just prowl about early mornings and evenings. You may not see any cats, but you will be seeing the wildest country left in these parts. And—" he leaned back and looked at us earnestly—"I think while you are here you ought to go to the bottom of the Canyon."

"You think we would find cougar there?" I asked.

"No—at least, it is unlikely. But I think you ought to go just for the experience."

Our ranger friend did not know it, but he had touched on a sore spot. I did not want to go to the bottom of Grand Canyon. Riding a mule over that long trail was the least of my desires, and I hoped no one would ask me to do it.

"We haven't all the time we need," I said to him unconvinced of the truth of my own argument. "The best photography is up here, and the most animals are here, so I guess we had better spend all our days here." Then I added weakly, "Much as we would like to go."

"Well," he said, "I still think you should."

I steered the conversation into other channels and hoped I would never hear another word on the subject.

In the cool of early evening, with a brilliant sunset gracing the sky, we walked down the trail to Bright Angel Point. The great old Canyon was weaving another masterpiece of silent beauty. Giny and I went out on a high rock and sat spellbound by the display before us. In the muted distance we could see the south rim of the Canyon, seeming to be so close at hand, but really ten miles away. We saw the sparkle of the lights of Canyon City and the dark outlines of San Francisco Mountains far in the south. In the gathering gloom of the Canyon depths we could see the Zoroaster Temple, Brahma Temple, Deva Temple, Uncle Jimmy—mountains that seem fashioned of mystic substance at this hour.

Presently I heard a sharp little voice. "A chipmunk!" I exclaimed. "What is he doing out at this time of evening?"

We listened, and the sound came again. "It is a chipmunk," agreed Giny. "One of the tiny-tinies," she said, using our pet name for the least chipmunk, the smallest of them all.

We started looking for the creature. The sound came from a few feet back of us where there were some huge boulders. Usually the least chipmunk is not difficult to see when he is calling, for with each note his tail flicks and this action catches the eye. "He must be right here," said Giny as we both rose looking for him. "Is that he on the rock?" No, that was a pine cone. Several other objects we accused of being chipmunks turned out otherwise. Still the call continued, and so did our search.

Unnoticed at first, a man had approached and stood watching us. Seeing what we were about, he moved forward as if to join in our search. "Good evening," I said to him. "There is a chipmunk calling and we are determined to find him."

"Maybe I can help you," he said in a strong, deep voice. With a purposeful stride he walked over to the large rock where we had been looking for our obscure visitor. "Come out of there, Bohunk," he said, jumping back of the rock. Now in place of the little chirps we heard a series of delighted giggles, and out came the man holding a five- or six-year-old boy high over his head. "Here is your chipmunk," he declared, pretending to handle the laughing child roughly. "He loves to fool people like that and if he doesn't stop it, I am going to pitch him headfirst right into that Canyon."

I could see them both clearly now and realized that they were Indians. The man was tall, strong, with high

cheekbones and dark skin. The youngster was small but wiry, his face beaming with a happiness that can only come from being loved a lot. He wore a headband with one feather in it.

"Listen here, you fake chipmunk," said Giny, stooping down to the youngster who was now showing some bashfulness, "where did you learn to imitate a chipmunk so perfectly?"

"I taught him," said the man, a bit of pride in his voice. He demonstrated his own ability by giving the call perfectly. "How does the chickaree go, Bohunk?"

Like all children, Bohunk had to be coaxed to perform. Finally he gave a right good imitation of a chickaree or red squirrel.

"And now, how does a marmot go?" the man asked.

There was more coaxing, and finally a call given that sounded more like a squeaky gate than a marmot.

"Ah, you can do better than that." The man picked him up and set him on his shoulder. "He's a little embarrassed at all this attention."

"Your son?" I asked.

"Yes, the Bohunk."

"Anyone as cute as that is probably the center of attention everywhere," I commented.

"Most of the time we do not see people," the father replied, tossing his son around like a ball, while the little one giggled delightedly. "We live in the woods."

"Navajo?" I asked.

"Hopi," he replied proudly.

I was impressed by the dignified bearing of the man and his clear correct English. Obviously he was a person of considerable culture and training. His son said something to him in very strange-sounding words. The father replied, and I realized they were conversing in their native tongue.

"Bohunk wants to know where you live," he interpreted.

"We are complimented at your interest, Bohunk," I

said to the youngster. "We live in Wisconsin, far, far away, where there are lots of woods and animals just as there are here."

The father translated my message for the youngster.

"He speaks no English?" Giny asked.

"Just a few words," replied the father. "I am teaching him Hopi first. He must learn that he is an Indian—" he hesitated a moment—"and will always be an Indian."

"His name?" asked Giny.

"Kona," said the father. "It is Hopi for chipmunk. I call him Bohunk most of the time—he's nothing but a rascal, a menace." He put the child on the ground, and the youngster ran away giving perfectly the calls of chipmunks, chickarees and marmots in rapid succession.

We sat down to resume our observation of the evening, and the Indian sat near us. Chipmunk gave Giny a start by running right up to the edge of the Canyon. She called to him to come back. "Don't worry," said the father. "He is like a mountain goat. Never happier than when he is at the edge of a thousand-foot cliff."

"My name is Sam Campbell," I said to him, feeling that we should be acquainted. "This is Mrs. Campbell. Could we have your name?"

"I am very glad to meet you," he said, bowing to Giny and extending his hand to me. "My legal name is John Corn. My real name was too hard for people to say."

In response to questions that followed, I told John Corn what was the purpose of our visit. He looks at me sharply. "What did you say your name is?" he asked.

"Sam Campbell."

"Oh, of course, of course," he said with fresh cordiality. "I have one of your books, *How's Inky?* I am telling Bohunk your story. Come here, Bohunk," he called to the boy. In his own language he told the boy who we were. "Inky?" he kept saying in a thin voice, "Inky?"

Now we were more important to him. He came up and shook hands with me and permitted Giny to take him in her arms.

There was a lengthy conversation between father and son in Hopi. "This is a great day for him," the father commented to me. "He calls you Inky's Papa, and to meet Inky's Papa is almost too much for him. You see we have had lots of animal pets. We never kill anything. He has never known what it is to abuse an animal, or to be abused."

There was no lack of interest and friendliness in our conversation now. Kona was somewhat overpowered by having Inky's Papa so close, and he hung to his father, peeking around shyly at Giny and me. I tried to lead John Corn to tell more about himself, but he avoided doing so. I felt there was a worth-while story here.

The Indian was most interested in the object of our mission. He was not too discouraging about finding mountain lions. "I know this land better than any of them," he said, and it did not seem to be boastfulness but just a statement of fact. "Maybe I can help you. You will be living at the Lodge?"

"Yes, except as we make expeditions back into the forest."

"Good. I can find you here."

He arose to go, taking his sleepy little Kona in his arms.

"One thing you should do while you are here," said John Corn, just as he was leaving.

"Yes?"

"Go to the bottom of the Canyon."

The darkness hid my scowl.

XII

IT'S A CONSPIRACY!

THE purple cloak of darkness still covered the world as we drove into the parking area at Point Imperial along the Canyon rim sixty-five miles east of the Lodge. On the northeastern horizon there was a soft gray glow, the first hint of morning, but elsewhere night reigned. We had expected to have the world to ourselves at this hour, but to our surprise our headlights revealed a dilapidated old car of ancient vintage and uncertain make. No one was in it, and it presented a lonely, deserted appearance.

"Looks like someone drove it this far, and it wouldn't go any farther," suggested Giny.

I felt the radiator and found it was quite warm, so it hadn't been at that spot long. The darkness ahead must hold other visitors, doubtless on a mission like our own.

We took our flashlights and cameras and followed the trail out on Point Imperial. There were two objectives to this early-morning trip: to see the sunrise from this vantage point and to catch in our cameras some record of two eagles frequently seen here.

Day comes rapidly once it gets under way. By the time we had reached the end of the trail, the world about us was taking form. In a cloudless northeastern sky the advance rays of the sun spread a golden glow halfway to the zenith. Far below in a cradle of silence lay the

Canyon, seemingly infinite in this indistinct lighting. A little stretch of the Colorado River was visible, its muddy waters now looking like a ribbon of gold in rich hues borrowed from the heavens. All about us lay those awesome magnitudes which leave thought only one choice: to retreat into humility and prayer.

"Listen!" whispered Giny, grasping my arm.

From far toward the vanishing stars came a faint, persistent cry.

"The eagles!" I exclaimed.

"Yes, but there is another sound. Listen."

Out of the shadows toward the edge of the Canyon flowed a low musical chant. It was of such positive rhythm that is seemed it must be paced by a tom-tom. The chant was composed of two blending human voices—one of high pitch, one of low. The effect of the strange sound was to deepen the wild beauty of our experience, and Giny and I stood fascinated.

Now the sun was peering over the horizon, the morning mists mellowing its rays so we could look directly at it. We could see the serpentine course of the Marble Canyon through which the Colorado enters Grand Canyon. In the purple distance to the south and east lay the other rim, fantastically high-lighted in flame color. Beyond this, looking like a landscape on the moon, stretched the Painted Desert. The Hopi call it Assa-Ma-Unda, Country of the Departed Spirits.

The chant increased in tone and quickened in rhythm, punctuated occasionally by a little shout. It was coming from back of a huge rock. Giny and I made our way toward the spot, cautiously selecting each step, for here a miscalculation might lead to an unanticipated journey into the depths.

At last we were in position to peek around the end of the big rock. There we saw our new friends John Corn and little Kona at the very edge of the Canyon. John was crouched down, Kona standing between his knees, both facing the rising sun, eyes closed, while they chanted as if the words and tones came from their very hearts. It was an impressive scene—the grandeur of the landscape

before us, the glow of the heavens, the eagles now plainly visible overhead, and these two children of nature voicing their appreciation in primitive sincerity.

It was not until the ceremony had come to a natural close and the two Indians turned to walk back to the trail that they discovered us.

"It was beautiful!" exclaimed Giny. "Beautiful! I hope you do not mind that we listened in."

John was embarrassed, and Kona tried to get into his trouser leg. "You are a big surprise," said the Indian, endeavoring to free himself from the youngster who clung like a porcupine. "If you enjoyed our performance, we are glad, though we do it just for ourselves—to make us realize we are part of all this."

"A Hopi tribal chant?" I asked.

"No, just ours. It belongs to Bohunk and me."

"Could you interpret it for us?" asked Giny. "That is, unless it is some secret you would rather not share."

John laughed. "No secret," he said. "I will try to give you the meaning, though such things seem so different in English than in Hopi. In your tongue it would be something like this:

> Rise, O Sun, symbol of the Great One.
> Bless your earth child with your light.
> Shine! Shine! Shine!
> Call the birds to singing,
> Call the trees and plants to growing,
> Call your people to work, O Great One.
> Keep their tongues straight,

Keep their hearts true.
Rise! Shine! Rise! Shine!
It is I, your child, O Great One, who calls.

"And, strangely," John went on, smiling, "when you sing those words at just the right time, the sun always obeys and comes up."

"Thank you," said Giny warmly. "Thank you for sharing such a precious thing with us. The way it all happened, it was a wonderful experience."

"Yes, this was an unexpected joy," I added. "We had come for another purpose." I pointed overhead to the two eagles which were quite plain.

"It is *Kwa'hu,* the eagle," declared John.

"Kwa'hu!" repeated Kona, letting go his hold on his father's trousers and looking upward. *"Kwa'hu! Kwa'hu!"* he called.

We returned to our cameras and focused the long-range lenses on the circling birds. They performed beautifully. Sometimes their effortless flight took them into the depths of the Canyon, then rising on an invisible updraft they would ascend into the clear blue sky overhead. They glided gracefully with never a flap of the wings. As they banked at certain angles we could plainly see white tails and white heads, identification marks of the bald or American eagle. After many minutes their circles took them toward the west.

"See, their circles are smaller," observed John. "It may be that they are nearing their nest. Shall we go find it?"

"Let's," agreed Giny, "unless it would be too much for little Chipmunk."

Kona had recovered from his embarrassment and was holding on to her hand. I could see a close companionship evolving between these two. The round-faced youngster whose eyes seemed to look at us from another world was creeping into Giny's heart, and she, with her keen understanding and love for children, was moving into his.

"Don't worry about him," John was saying. "He will still be running circles around us when we are worn out."

Under John's intuitive guidance we went quite a distance through difficult country. Travel wasn't easy. It was a rocky, rugged land, coated with a cool forest of ponderosa pines and spotted with clusters of aspens. We held to the direction in which the eagles disappeared, and soon our efforts were rewarded. In the top of a leafless pine on the summit of a high, rocky ridge we discovered their nest.

Eagles mate for life, and year after year the pair will return to the same nest. They will enlarge it with new material and strengthen it each season. The nest before us must have been long in the making—perhaps fifteen years. Dry branches over an inch in thickness had been anchored securely in the crotch of the tree until a mass had accumulated over twelve feet in height.

Perhaps it is possible to approach an eagle's nest without the sharp-eyed birds seeing you, but I have never been able to do it. That day when we realized we were actually approaching the nest we tried every trick we knew. We covered the camera with a dark cloth so no flash of light from the metal would be seen. We circled and came toward the nest tree with the sun at our backs. We kept in the shadows of trees and took cover back of bushes wherever possible.

Kona was a star. He was so silent and so clever at concealing himself that only his father knew where he was most of the time. Yet, with all our caution, long before we were within camera range the huge birds had detected us and were uttering their alarm cries. They circled above the treetops, looking down at us, trying to determine what we were doing. How graceful and powerful they looked up there, with wing spreads of fully five feet! We abandoned caution now and moved quickly toward the nest tree.

"Small wonder he is our national bird," commented Giny. "Where could you find anything that would suggest better the love of freedom and the determination to defend it than in the eagle?"

We kept watching the nest closely, quite certain that we hadn't seen all of this family. Our camera was recording the maneuvers of the two birds. Twice they dipped low over us, acting as if they meant to attack, but did not. Eagles have been known to attack men in defense of their young, but only when their nests were being violated. Stories of their viciousness have been greatly exaggerated.

Kona showed his utter fearlessness of the birds, walking right out into the open, holding up his hands and calling, *"Kwa'hu! Kwa'hu!"* He added some words his father interpreted for me. "He is asking *Kwa'hu* to come down and sit on his hand," he said.

"Kona," laughed Giny, "he wouldn't fit! You'd better get a canary."

"He would even try to make it an ostrich," said his father. "The Bohunk!"

Curiosity is universally present in nature. Presently we witnessed the effect of curiosity down in the eagle's nest. In spite of the warning cries of the parent birds, junior came peeking over the side! He just had to see what all the shouting was about. He struggled until he was perched on the edge of the nest where he could get a good look at everything. His parents went wild. They scolded him and made bombing runs at him, but he stayed there just the same.

Kona was so excited to see the little one he jumped up and down and screamed. Eagle Junior let out a few calls himself, just to be a part of everything. I put the six-inch lens on my camera and leveled it at him. That was more than the parent birds could stand. The thing looked too much like a gun for their comfort. One of the older birds—I could not tell whether father or mother, as they are identical in markings—took Junior to task. Scolding severely, the parent bird landed on the nest beside Junior and gave him as neat a spanking as I ever witnessed. The wings of the older bird came down on his back with force, and Junior realized that he had gone a step too far in his defiance and disobedience. In the midst of a shower of blows he retreated down into the nest, and we didn't see him again. We felt sorry for Junior, but what an opportunity he had provided for my camera!

"Did you get all of that?" asked John.

"I surely did," I answered, laughing. "I wouldn't take anything for that picture."

We made our way back after this. Kona did tire and had to hitchhike a ride on his father's broad shoulders. It was near noon when we arrived at the old car belonging to our Indian friends.

"Doesn't look like much," John commented, "but it gets us places, eh, Bohunk?"

Kona pulled his father down to his level to ask a question. John murmured something and looked up at us. Kona whispered more in his ear. John replied in his native tongue, then looked at us again. Kona demanded his ear again and looked to be almost at the point of tears.

"Well," said John, "I'll ask them anyway. Kona wants to know if you would come to dinner at our camp. I tell him you have good food at the Lodge, and my cooking is not . . ."

"But we would love it," broke in Giny. "Please let us come."

"Would you really?" John's face brightened as he looked at us. "I would be happy to have you. Besides—" he looked down at his boy—"besides, it is good for Kona to be with you. He sees so much of me—he needs other people, especially a woman."

"His mother—?" I started to question.

"Gone," burst John with an emphasis that silenced any further inquiry in that direction. His eyes lighted with pain and the lines of his face deepened.

"Could you have us tomorrow night?" I asked, retreating from the subject which was apparently delicate if not dangerous.

"Yes, indeed," replied John, shaking himself out of the mood that had struck him so suddenly. "Come early. There is a white-tailed squirrel back of our camp, and you may be able to photograph him."

Kona was asking something again now, and John had to stoop to him. There was an exchange of words in Hopi, then John said in English, "You ask him. You know how to say that—you ask him." Kona had to be encouraged, but at last he ventured three words. "You—go—down?" he asked, his eyes reflecting the question.

"I go down—where?"

"You—go—down?" he repeated, with emphasis.

"I go down?"

"He wants to know if you are going down into the Canyon. He wants to go along," John clarified things.

I surprised the breath out of Kona by catching him up and giving him a mock spanking. "Don't you ask me that, you little Bohunk," I said, shaking him while he giggled. "No, I am not going down in the Canyon, do you understand? And I don't want to be asked about it either."

Kona caught the idea, and also realized it got him some extra attention to say, "You—go—down?" So while we completed arrangements for our dinner at their camp, he kept peeking at me from behind his father, from behind our automobiles, from behind Giny, and from behind trees, calling, "You—go—down?" the question always followed by a rivulet of giggles. This didn't end until his father packed him in his car and started away. And even then he stuck his beaming face out the window and said, "You—go—down?"

"What impression did you get about Kona's mother?" asked Giny as we drove toward the Canyon Lodge.

"I am not sure," I replied, puzzled. "John's reaction was strange, a mixture of sadness and anger. We had better leave that subject alone unless he opens it."

Back at the Lodge it seemed to me that everyone had caught on to Kona's little joke. "I have been thinking about your pictures, Mr. Campbell," said the manager. "It seems to me they wouldn't be complete unless you go down to the bottom of the Canyon."

"We have been thinking about it," I answered with a weak smile, but I didn't tell him what I had been thinking about it.

"I missed you," said the waitress who usually served us. "Have you been to the bottom of the Canyon?"

I shook my head.

"Not yet, eh? Well, no doubt you will be going down soon."

Well, if she didn't have any doubt about it, I did.

The cabin girls, the bellboys, the bus drivers all thought I ought to go to the bottom of Grand Canyon. I had never had so many people interested in where I was to go in my life and I didn't appreciate the attention.

"But, do you suppose we ought to go down there just for the experience?" asked Giny.

"You, too, Brutus?" I replied. "Giny, I do not want to go down in that Canyon. Do you know how far it is? Fourteen miles to Phantom Ranch—fourteen miles! You have to ride on a mule all the way."

"Well," she persisted, "others have done it."

"Yes, and when they come back they can't stand up and they can't sit down. Giny, I don't want to go down there. To begin with, I am not a rider. I was raised in a canoe country and I'll handle one of those things as well as the next fellow. But I have been on horses only twice in my life and I was sorry each time I got on one of the critters. I'm not built for it, I tell you."

"Don't you remember our rule for traveling?" she went on. "We are to ask ourselves: 'a year from now, what will we wish we had done today?' That has kept us from getting lazy and missing a lot of things."

"All right," I said with finality. "I'll take you at your own words. A year from now I'll be plenty thankful I didn't go down in that Canyon on a mule. So-o-o-o, that settles it once and for all. I am not going to the bottom of Grand Canyon, and I hope I don't hear another word about it."

There was a knock at our cabin door. A boy had brought an air-mail letter from Hi-Bub and Tony. They wrote:

This is just a note to tell you all is well. Lots happening, and a long letter will be coming soon. We met someone in town who had been to Grand Canyon, and what do you think—he didn't go down to the bottom. Guess he was afraid of the mules. We told him you would go down. Write us all about it. Greetings from Zipper, Zowie, Zanie, Zinnia, and the Seven Secrets. Sincerely, Hi-Bub and Tony.

I finished reading this aloud and then looked at Giny. "Mind if I laugh?" she asked, and, whether I did or not, she did.

XIII

GOOFUS!

WE CAME early in the day to the public camp site. Our dinner with John and Kona was to be in the evening, but we wanted to get pictures of the white-tailed squirrel the Indians had seen.

Their camp was in the midst of a circle of sturdy pines. The old car stood at one side. They had an umbrella-type tent of good size. The camp was neat and clean. To our great surprise and delight we found John sitting before an easel painting a canvas! He seemed a little embarrassed as we came up to him.

"There was such a wonderful effect of mist in the woods this morning," he said, after greetings had been exchanged. "I was trying to catch it with my brush."

"John, you have done it!" exclaimed Giny, looking at his work. "It is wonderful!"

"No," said John, smiling. "It is good, but it isn't wonderful. I am not as good a painter as I would like to be."

"But this is fine, John," I insisted, looking at his canvas. "You have that feeling of mystery and distance that only a nature lover would detect. This woman does so much for the scene," I added, pointing to a figure set far back in the picture, obscure in the mists. "It gives a spiritual tone to it. Was someone there?"

"The product of my own fancy," answered John.

123

Kona came out of the tent at this moment and got our attention with a giggle. In his hands was another painting showing the Grand Canyon as seen from Bright Angel Point. "You—go—down?" he said, holding it up to us, his eyes twinkling mischievously.

"Kona!" I exclaimed. "Are you going to tease me today?"

Likely I would have picked him up and given him the mock spanking he was expecting, except for John's quick move. He knelt beside the boy, looking him right in the eyes, talking slowly and earnestly in Hopi. Kona listened closely, uttered a few words of his own which John answered, and then nodded his head understandingly. "I do not want him to carry that too far or be disrespectful," the father said to me by way of explanation. "Little ones sometimes don't know where to stop."

"But it was in fun, John," I protested. "I think it is cute for him to tease."

"To do it once, yes," replied the Indian. "To carry it on would not be wise. He understands now and he only wants to do the right thing. I'm sure he will not say that again."

And Kona never did! His obedience was remarkable. He did not feel coerced or frustrated, only advised. "We just work out things together," John said.

Giny and I now examined the painting. "You are a surprising man, John," I commented. "I admire your talents and your accomplishments. Do you have more of this kind of work?"

Almost reluctantly the Indian led us into the tent. Here

on a cot along one wall were a dozen or more paintings, some tastefully framed. Kona was in several of them, his tiny face and expressive eyes so well done it was obvious that John had portrait ability. One rather large canvas the Indian had picked up quickly as we entered the tent. I saw little of it, but had the impression of a young woman, tall, beautiful and handsomely gowned. "It is something I didn't do very well," said John as he wrapped it up. "I would rather you didn't see it."

Kona was right proud of his father's work. He diretced our attention to one after another of his favorites. The pictures invited study. In the shadows and distances there were subtle objects found only by close attention. The subjects were Canyon landscapes, desert scenes, flowers and cloud effects. In most of them I found again that filmy figure noted in the picture John was working on this morning, always subtle and obscure.

"I should tell you that this is the way Kona and I pay our bills," John explained. "My paintings are not art collector's items, but they have provided the means for travel through the West in the last few months."

"Who are your purchasers?" asked Giny.

"Just those we meet. Yesterday a fellow camper bought one before he left. A sale always comes about when we need it."

"There are several of these I would be interested in," I declared. "This one of Bright Angel Point . . ."

"No!" John interrupted me. "No—not now, anyway. You may wish to buy it just to help me. Anyway, you had better get to work on those squirrels."

Apparently there was nothing more to be said about the paintings. Getting directions from John, we made our way through the woods to the place where the white-tailed squirrel had been seen.

Of all the exasperating, teasing, tantalizing scamps I ever hunted with my camera, the Kaibab squirrel is the worst! We found the one our Indian friends had discovered about a ten-minute walk from their camp. The squirrel was on the ground when we saw him, 100 yards ahead of us. He had a beautiful white tail and he kept flicking it with pride as he went about digging, scratching and nosing around as squirrels do.

Long before we were within camera range, the squirrel noticed us and started up a giant pine tree. We named him Goofus. He clung to the heavy ridge of bark, waving his tail and watching us closely. As we drew nearer, camera all ready for action, he very unaccommodatingly ran around on the other side of the tree and then peeked at us.

"Come, Goofus," called Giny. "Come on, Goofus, you're going to be in the movies."

Goofus was convinced to the contrary. He ran up the tree a few feet and then looked at us again, only his head showing. We circled to the left and so did he, keeping the trunk of the tree between us. We circled to the right. So did Goofus. Then Giny went one way, and I went the other. Goofus went up on a huge limb that concealed all of him except his head and kept watching us. I tried climbing a neighboring tree and just got where I could see him plainly when he raced to the top of the one he was in. Away up there in the top branches he felt safely concealed, so he went to sleep. We could see a portion of his white tail hanging down from his perch, but that was all.

"We'll just have to wait," said Giny.

Waiting is one of the best things you do in animal photography. A half hour later Goofus moved for the first time. Giny had the binoculars on him at the moment and she warned me to get ready. I took my station back of the camera and leveled the six-inch lens in the direction of Goofus. He sat up, yawned, stretched, straightened out the hair in his tail—and went to sleep again! Another hour passed, and another! Still Goofus slumbered on.

Giny thoughtfuly had brought two sandwiches along, and we ate these within sight of the squirrel tree. Surely Goofus would get hungry too and have to move around. He did. He went to the very top of the tree and got a pine cone. Seated in a crotch where only occasional glimpses of him were possible, he tore the cone apart, ate the seeds, dropping the trimmings on us, and then went back to sleep. No pictures!

Two more hours passed. Giny and I took turns looking up at the squirrel. One neck alone couldn't endure the strain. We tried a ruse, bidding him good-by and walking away as if we were defeated. When we came back he was in the same spot in the top of his big ponderosa pine.

The sun was getting low in the west now, and we had spent practically the entire day under that tree, without taking a single foot of film. In a few minutes the forest shadows would be too heavy, and the chance for pictures would be gone. We heard a voice behind us.

"We were getting worried about you." It was John and

Kona. "Wondered if the white-tail had carried you off. Are you having any success?"

"Not one bit!" I ejaculated, and I told them how unco-operative Goofus had been.

"You get ready with your camera," said John. "Let's try something." He began giving the call of the chickaree, in which Kona joined him. Now, the chickaree is a hated rival of the Kaibab squirrel. As the annoying sounds reached Goofus, he straightened up and gave some saucy answer. John and Kona hurled squirrel insults at him. He fired right back at them. As the banter continued, Goofus forgot all about us and came forth searching for this chickaree that dared venture into his domain. He ran right out on the end of a branch, regardless of the fact that he was in full sunlight and my camera was grinding away at him. Irritated beyond all endurance, he uttered several notes of defiance and scampered down to the ground, heading in our direction. Changing rapidly from one lens to another, I recorded distant shots, close-ups, intermediates, all perfectly posed and in perfect lighting. We giggled and we laughed and we took yards of pictures. Then old Goofus, not twenty-five feet from us, discovered that he had been deceived. Chattering invectives at us, he raced up his tree to the highest crotch.

"O.K., Old Top," I called him, "call me anything you want to. Pictures like these are worth all the abuse you can give."

We walked back to John's camp, Goofus scolding after us. John was laughing, and Kona was squealing with delight.

"We are certainly indebted to you two chickarees," Giny said. "Goofus had us just about whipped."

John's dinner was fine. We ate out under the pines, watching the soft, pastel shades of evening settle on the forest. What we were most impressed with was the

absolute cleanliness which prevailed at this camp. Kona was washed and thoroughly polished before dinner, and the amazing thing was that he liked it.

We all took part in washing the dishes, and then John built a huge, cheery campfire. The north rim of the Canyon is some 8,000 feet above sea level, and even summer evenings have a frosty feel to them. We drew close to the fire. Conversation drifted to our home in Wisconsin, and we answered many questions about our friendly animals. Kona seemed to catch some of the conversation, though John frequently interpreted facts for him. How big was Inky? Were Rack and Ruin still there? How about Bobette? We told of Zipper, Zowie, Zanie and Zinnia while Kona pressed his father for the stories in a tongue he understood. His giggles were the same in English as they would be in Hopi, however. Feeling safe with these people and at this great distance, we told of the Seven Secrets of Somewhere Lake.

"You know," said John after a period of silence, "I once hoped I would never meet you."

We looked at him questioningly.

"Well, I was afraid you were not real. I did not want to be disillusioned. Now I know. You are real." He paused a moment in deep thought, then continued in quiet tones. "I am proud to be Hopi," he said with feeling. "Our real name is Hopitu Shinimu, and it means 'The Peaceful People.' Usage has shortened it to Hopi. We have always been kind to the animal people with whom we share the world. We have not been fighters, destroyers. I am proud to be Hopi."

There was another period of silence. The fire burned merrily, the crackling of the dry pine wood echoing back through the woods. Kona silently moved up to Giny, and her arm slipped around him.

"He is tired," observed John. "Bohunk, is it time for our good-night song?"

Kona nodded and came to his father. John got to his knees and circled his arms about the lad as they both faced the fire. Their eyes closed and simultaneously they began a chant. Once Kona forgot the words and had to be prompted, but he spoke the difficult Hopi sentences clearly and well. It was an impressive little ceremony, and we were sorry when it was done.

"May we have an interpretation?" asked Giny.

"This is as near as I can give it to you," John replied.

> "O Great One, another day is done;
> We have seen the glory of another sun;
> Now the evening shadows are falling,
> Now your peace comes to the earth.
> Give me, O Great One, of your rest,
> In sleep prepare me for tomorrow!"

As John was speaking, Kona moved quietly back to Giny. The union of the two was complete now. She took him in her arms, and while the shadows of the campfire flames danced upon them, he went to sleep. John's lips spread into a warm smile as he looked at them. "That is what he needs," he said, though his words seemed intended only for himself.

"John," I said, "you fascinate me and puzzle me at the same time. Your use of the English language—that was not learned in the great spaces of the West."

"No," he said, laughing a little, "no, it was not. Perhaps I owe you a little explanation. I was born in the Indian world, but I was educated at your schools. My people, the Hopi, were builders, making houses ages ago out of mud and wood. I wanted to be a builder. So when schooling was available to me, I took all I could get, majoring in art and architecture, finally graduating from college.

You see, I have learned more about the language and ways of your people than I did of my own."

John was thoughtful for a few minutes. He sat staring into the campfire while he toyed with his memories, the tense muscles of his bronze face causing little valleys in his cheeks. When he spoke again, it was as if he had lost consciousness of our presence and was addressing his words to the fire.

"My experience has been a trying one. Perhaps it was my fault, I do not know. Maybe I should have been wiser. When my education was completed, my heart was singing with high idealism. I was to do great works, to see beautiful structures built of my designs and plans." He laughed. "I had been taught that all men are created equal—that the color of the skin and the kind of ancestors make no difference. I had not been out in the world long until I commenced to realize this was not yet true. I found that I was not wholly accepted by white society, that opportunities were denied me not because I lacked ability, but because I was born an Indian."

John got to his feet. He rearranged the fire, and then walked back into the night to obtain more wood. I stared after him, feeling the strength and sadness of his story. It was not the first time I had known the plight of the Indian who is educated out of one way of life to find he is not accepted in another. John placed two large logs on the fire and resumed his seat.

"Am I boring you with my personal troubles?" he asked.

"No, John, no," I assured him. "I am complimented that you will talk to me this way."

"I believe I need to talk," he said. "I have thought and thought until I go around in circles. The Hopi say, 'evil thrives in secret darkness; it disappears in sunlight.' If I had been the only one in my picture, the problem would have been easier. I could have taken the rebuffs and disappointments and kept working to reach a level of accomplishment where my work would speak for itself. Men of all races and colors have done that. However, I had met Polimana!"

He spoke the name with the same emphasis which had been in evidence when he told me the previous day that Kona's mother was gone. He shifted his position, his lips drew tight, and his eyes flashed in the firelight. Steadying himself, he continued: "That is my name for her—Polimana, the Butterfly Girl. She was beautiful, and we were so in love we could recognize no barrier. We were married, over the objections of her people and mine. We established our home in a big city. We were happy too, and soon Kona came along to make us still happier.

"But the problem of work became more and more difficult for me, as did the social problem. Neighbors and friends were nice to us, but we always had the feeling they were doing it because they thought they ought to. It was a constant strain, and sometimes I found Polimana crying." There was another pause, then he went on. "Surely, I gave her little to be proud of. I worked as a laborer; I drove a truck—did anything I could to make a living. Her family had always lived at respected levels and had fine records of accomplishment. What hurt us worst was to realize the handicap that Kona would carry."

"But, John," I broke in. "There have been people with Indian blood who have reached high levels in America. Vice-President Curtis, for instance."

"Yes, I know that," he agreed. "But for every one who has broken through the opposing forces there are a hundred who have been broken by them."

There was a long period of silence now. Giny drew Kona more tightly to her. John rose to his feet and stood with his back to the fire, so we could not see his face. After many minutes he spoke.

"Well, we became desperate," he said. "We came West, hoping that the Indian world might offer us better opportunity for happiness than we had found in the city. I planned to turn to my painting. We went through pitiful poverty. Poor Polimana! The change was too much for her. She had been raised in luxury and in the West she was plunged into most crude surroundings. She struggled bravely, but the task was too great. One day—" he had to pause and steady his voice—"one day she left while I was out seeking work. There was a note saying she could stand it no longer. She asked me to care for Kona, that he would fare better in my world than in hers. She gave me instructions on what to do for him and said, though her heart was breaking, that if I wished him to have another mother, she would give me my freedom. She asked me never to try to find her, that she was ashamed of what she was doing and unworthy of Kona or me."

"You have never heard from her since?" I asked.

"Twice," he said. "Two letters have come giving me additional instruction about Kona. But they gave no address where I could reach her. I have written in care of her people, but the letter was returned unopened."

"And so you have traveled about with Kona, earning your way by the sale of pictures." I carried on the story for him. "How long since Polimana left?"

"Two years," said John. "Two years and sixteen days. I am determined that Kona have a chance to be Hopi. Soon he will reach school age and he will learn the culture of the white race. But I am teaching him Hopi. I hope he finds such great joy in it he will never be tempted to leave it."

"And are you bitter against Polimana?" asked Giny, in a whisper so that she would not disturb Kona.

John gripped his cheeks with his hand. "No," he said positively. "No, sometimes I am angry that she could leave *him*. But as I think and think and think, I understand her position."

"And she is still the central figure in your heart," I observed, "and that fact makes you paint her into your pictures. She is the misty figure, is she not?"

John's answer was a delayed nod. He drew himself to his full height, with an air that savored of pride. "The Hopi say that 'a man is weak indeed who asks another to help bear his sorrow.' Please forgive me."

"John," I said earnestly, "we are honored by your confidence."

XIV

A PRINCE POSES

FROM several people we heard the report of the Prince of Cape Royal. He was a magnificent buck of the black-tailed mule deer and was seen regularly in that locality in early mornings and evenings. Cape Royal is a concentrate of spectacular scenery lying forty-five miles to the east of the Lodge area, twenty miles south of Point Imperial.

We went seeking the Prince. The first day we were about Cape Royal from dawn to dusk, but caught not a sight of him. The second day the results were the same. The third day we nearly caught him. A ranger naturalist saw him just before we arrived in the area, and other travelers later found him a few miles to the north, but we missed him.

The next afternoon, the fourth day of our effort to photograph this great creature, our opportunity came. We were busy recording a lovely blacktail family—a young buck, a doe and two fawns. They had been entertaining us very highly. We found them grazing atop a small hill. As we approached, Giny whispered excitedly, "Sam, look!" She directed my attention far to the right of the place where our family of blacktails were grazing. There stood a buck of such startling proportions we knew it must be the Prince. He was in full sunlight, silhouetted against the Grand Canyon!

It was the kind of picture of which a photographer dreams and for which he prays. Excitement gripped me, no doubt the same feeling that hunters call buck fever.

My camera, mounted on the tripod, with long-range lens attached, was sloping over my shoulder. But I couldn't think what to do with it.

"Now, don't get excited," I said inanely to Giny. "Let's do everything just right."

"Who's excited?" she asked. "Why don't you set up your camera?"

"Yes, yes," I whispered back, "I was just going to. Quiet now."

I spread the tripod legs, then promptly stumbled on one of them, and Giny caught the camera before it struck the ground. The Prince looked at us calmly, but held his pose. With my growing case of buck fever, he looked about the size of an elephant, his huge antlers spread like a Christmas tree.

I got the tripod straightened up. "Is everything all right?" I asked Giny. "Let's keep our heads about us now."

"Yes," said Giny with a smile. " 'Most everything is all right, but do you know you have the camera pointed the wrong way? You would take a picture of your own eye, not the Prince."

"Surely," I said, still more confused. "I was just going to turn it around. Quiet now, I am going to shoot."

"Do you mind if I take the lens cap off?" said Giny, calmly reaching over and removing the rubber covering that would have given me a perfectly blank strip of film if it had been forgotten. "Now let's check the focus and exposure."

"Giny," I said pleadingly, "you take the picture. My hands are too unsteady. Maybe I am a little bit excited."

"A little bit?" she asked, and I stood back while she calmly completed preparations and then recorded the great buck.

How the Prince performed for us! He began moving forward with a fancy parade step like the strutting of a trained show horse. Still in full range of the camera, he quickened his pace, finally disappearing into the distance in a series of magnificent leaps.

"Oh!" I gasped, leaning against a tree for support. "Look at the camera. Check the aperture and focus. If there was anything wrong and we didn't get that picture, don't tell me about it now. Don't tell me about it for days—I couldn't stand it."

"Nothing wrong," insisted Giny, looking closely at the camera. "Everything is as it should be, and you have your pictures. Now relax!"

She burst out laughing. "You, Sam Campbell, who have lived most of your life in the woods and made thousands of feet of animal pictures. You—with buck fever!"

Back at the Lodge there was a thick letter from the boys awaiting us. We opened the envelope eagerly. The letter was written by both boys, their contributions alternating, typographical errors plentiful.

Tony says:

> A letter from Hi-Bub and Tony,
> Better expect something phoney,
> Some of it's news,
> Some of it's views,
> But most of it's common balonga!

Hi-Bub says:

What is this fellow Tony you left with me anyway? He looks human but he acts like a bottomless pit. I keep pouring food into him from morning to night, and he just gets skinnier and acts hungrier. He only eats one meal a day, but it lasts from the time he gets up until he goes to bed. Through the night he chews on the blanket. I have to watch or he would eat the animal food.

Tony says:
Zounds, the knave seeks to cover up his own faults. I have eaten so many eggs I am nothing by a two-legged omelet. It is all he can cook! Fried eggs, boiled eggs, scrambled eggs, poached eggs, raw eggs—by the eternal I am beginning to cackle.

Hi-Bub says:
I am maligned, slandered, misquoted! Does he mention the fifteen pancakes he ate this very morning—my culinary masterpieces? Does he show gratitude that I slave over a hot stove while he wanders through the forest composing poetry? Does he give thanks for my service beyond the call of duty, even to the baking of cakes and pies?

Tony says:
Pies—he says, pies? There has been but one pie, and it is a question as to whether it merits the title. True, he called it a pie. It was shaped like a pie and it was baked in a pie plate. But, as Shakespeare would say, that don't make it no pie. When it came out of the oven it had a finish on it like a new car. The ingredients he used would make the most marvelous armor plate. When we tapped the crust with a knife it sounded like drumming on top of the stove. We tried to cut it and the knife edge bent over as if it were made of cheese. We finally pried the two crusts apart with a screw driver and ate the filling with a spoon!

Hi-Bub says:
Ingrate—if I had time I'd go home to mother. How-

ever, this epistle is not intended to be a gastronomic dissertation, whatever that is. Stand by for important news! At least three of the Seven Secrets have taken food from our hands! Zanie, myself and Tony (mentioned in the order of importance) have been to Somewhere Lake at least once every day, sometimes twice. We named the beavers after the seven dwarfs: Sleepy, Grumpy, Sneezy, Doc, Dopey, Bashful and Happy—but the trouble is Sleepy might be Grumpy, Sneezy might be Sleepy, and Grumpy might be anyone. We can't tell them apart. They wouldn't have much to do with us at first, but we kept bringing them apples, doughnuts, graham crackers, carrots, whole wheat bread. Zanie finally bridged the gap. One evening he went up to the beavers in that doggy way of his. Three of them let him come right up to them. While he was there, we crawled out. He seemed to give them some assurance that everything was all right. We laid on the ground and reached toward the beavers offering pieces of apple. Two of them finally took bites! Then each visit they became more accustomed to us, until now they come out to meet us every time we go to Somewhere Lake.

Tony cuts in:

What he isn't telling is that just when we had them nice and trained, so they would feed right by our feet, he had to fall in the lake and scare the flat tails off all of them. You never heard so much slapping and diving in all your life. He dripped through the woods all the way home, and it took two days to calm the Seven Secrets down again. Anyway, we counted six trees that they have cut down, and they have started to cut fourteen others. No houses showing up yet. The water of Somewhere Lake is getting clearer all the time, so apparently they are keeping the springs cleaned out.

Hi-Bub again:

Before Zanie gets too much praise, I want to register a complaint against that purp. In fact, I have a number of complaints. He has carried away Tony's slippers, and we can't find them. That isn't so bad, but he has hidden mine too. He took my best tie and ran all around the woods dragging it through the brush. By the time we caught him the tie looked fit for a hard-times party. He certainly keeps life from getting monotonous.

Speaking of complaints, I have one to register against Tony. He seems to have forgotten the secret of silence in the woods. Last night, almost at midnight, he gave out such a terrible yell that Zowie ran away and didn't even come back for breakfast!

Now comes Tony:

Yes, I did—and I wonder why! Who wouldn't yell if he stepped on a porcupine with his bare feet? Hi-Bub put Salt down in my bed under the covers, and Salt went to sleep there. I climbed into bed and rammed my bare feet right against him! Certainly I yelled.

Rebuttal from Hi-Bub:

Well, maybe I did put just one little porcupine in his bed. Did he have to make such a fuss? Anyway, I wouldn't have done it except that he put a frog in my shoe the day previous. You didn't hear me yell did you?—or did you?

More from Tony:

Aside from that, things are going smoothly. Zowie has become friendly with Zinnia. Zipper gets peppier each day. She is wading out in the water often, eating lily leaves and looking toward the mainland. We think she will try the swim soon. Chipmunks and squirrels are getting along as unpleasantly as usual. Zanie has an awful job on his hands with them. He doesn't want anything to fight with anything else. Yesterday when the chipmunks were trying to get some cracked corn and the squirrels bothered them, Zanie parked himself right beside the corn. The chipmunk was feeding two feet from his nose, and the squirrels didn't dare come near. Zanie stayed there until the chipmunks had all they wanted, then he moved away to give the squirrels a chance. He is kind of a United Nations all in himself.

Hi-Bub again:
    EXTRA! FLASH! SPECIAL! We saw our first baby raccoons of the summer. Last night a mother and six woolly youngsters showed up. Were they cute! They looked like little muffs with legs on. They liked some raisins and bread we tossed out to them. We think the mother is Andrea.

Finale by Tony:
                There's the report for you folks
                From this land of egg whites and yolks;
                There's no more to tell,
                We're getting on swell
                In spite of our bum little jokes.
                            Sincerely yours,
                                Hi-Bub and Tony

"Oh, that's wonderful," exclaimed Giny as she finished reading the letter. "Hi-Bub is finding himself, isn't he? What a fine companion Tony is!"

"There is something more, on the back of the last sheet, isn't there?" I asked, noticing some additional writing.

There was something more, but it was disturbing to say the least. Hi-Bub had added a postscript:

Dear folks, hope you don't mind our foolishness, and that this letter brings you news in spite of the way it is written. We are having a grand time. I wanted to tell you that I have met the most wonderful fellow. His name is Bill, and he says he gave you both Zipper and Zowie....

Giny and I looked at each other with concern.

He stopped in one day when he was fishing in the lake. He is crazy about animals. If you don't object I would like to tell him of the Seven Secrets and take him with us to Somewhere Lake.

"Oh, no!" I exclaimed. "Hi-Bub must not tell Bill, of all people."

"How can you stop him?" asked Giny

"A telegram," I said. "Let's go to the Lodge at once."

We were able to call Cedar City and send this wire:

Hi-Bub—don't tell anyone our secret. This very important. Letter follows.

Giny now offered a suggestion. "After dinner, let's go over to the campground and share this letter with John and Kona," she said. "They would get a lot of pleasure out of it."

Later we went to the campground. John and Kona were gone—tent, car and all!

XV

THE PLOT THICKENS

WE dispatched an air-mail letter to Hi-Bub to follow up our brief telegram.

"I believe it isn't necessary to tell him too much about Bill," Giny commented as I was typing the letter. "He has taken a liking to Bill, and maybe the friendship would be good for both of them. I suggest you just impress the fact on him that no one must be told about the beavers."

I wrote:

There is only one way to keep a secret, and that is to entrust it to no one. Therefore don't tell Bill—don't even hint that you have a secret. THIS IS IMPORTANT!

Giny and I were both puzzled and distressed by the sudden departure of John Corn and Kona. There had not been the slightest hint of such plans during our campfire visit together the previous night. In fact, we had talked of more camera hunting together and the purchase of several of John's paintings. The supervisor of the campground could give us no information as to where they went. He saw their heavily packed car leaving early that morning and was rather surprised, for they had intended to stay for some time.

"Kona!" mused Giny. "Bless his little Indian heart, it seems as if some of the Grand Canyon has gone with him."

"Let's hope their trail is a circular one," I commented, "and that whatever way it starts out, it leads back to us."

We went back to the tree where our white-tailed squirrel lived. He was there and he tantalized us in the same manner as before. But there was no one to chatter like a chickaree and cause him to move around, so we got no pictures. We made another early-morning trip to Point Imperial to photograph the dawn, but there was no one to chant to the sun, so it rose behind a cloud.

A week passed, and intense activity began to cover over our longing for our friends. One evening we went to the great meadows north of the Lodge. In fairly good light and within easy range of our camera we saw a coyote come trotting out of the forest. He engaged in a brief scuffle with something in the grass and then straightened up with a small snake in his mouth. Holding his trophy proudly, he turned and trotted into the woods again. It was a picture worth having. The sun sank slowly behind peaks to the west, heavy shadows advancing across the meadow. In the dimming light, many deer came quietly into the open spaces, grazing as they moved forward. We counted 175 of the graceful creatures within sight of the spot where we stood!

We received a reply from Hi-Bub. He wrote:

Sorry if I disturbed you in asking permission to tell Bill our secret. A telegram and an air-mail letter! I guess I found out it is important to keep quiet. All right, mum is the word! Now I have a favor to ask. All my life I have dreamed about being at the bottom of the Grand Canyon. When you get down there, will you take some extra pictures for me? And will you tell that river not to go away until I get there—for I am coming some time, sure!

"That's all propaganda!" I declared. "Even Hi-Bub is scheming against me."

About the Lodge the great conspiracy continued unabated. A party had just returned from a trip to the bottom of the Canyon. They enthused over the experience.

"If they could do it, surely we could," Giny commented. She wasn't on my side at all.

"I have no doubt that we *could* do it," I replied. "No doubt we could slide down Mount McKinley too—but what would it do to us? Just look at those folks. Everyone walks as if he were astraddle a redwood log. There are lots of things I won't be able to do in this world. I presume I'll never go to the South Pole. I will never be a flagpole sitter. Riding a mule into Grand Canyon is just another one of those things."

Giny smiled.

The same evening the hotel manager sent for us. He introduced us to a most impressive-looking man named Jack Burns. Jack stood over six feet high and looked almost that broad. He wore chaps and spurs and a Western hat the size of a small swimming pool. When he shook hands with me, my hand utterly disappeared in his and came out feeling as if it had been in a wringer. His voice was gentle, his manner to Giny most courteous, but I had the conviction that I would just as soon be on his side in any argument.

"I wanted you to meet Jack," the manager was saying, "because he is in charge of the service to the bottom of the Canyon."

"Yes," said Jack, while I swallowed hard. "We can fix you up and be mighty happy to do it."

"Well, I hope we can find the time to do it," I said, with one of those *ha-ha*'s that has no merriment in it at all. "We have so much to do and so little time. . . ."

"No better way to use your time than in the greatest adventure in the world," said Jack in his best drawl. Then without giving me a chance to say any more, he went into his sales talk. I never faced anything like it. We have heard of the man who sold the national capitol to a stranger—I believe Jack could sell it back again. Nothing I could say created the least doubt in his thought that we were going down in that Canyon. While I was interposing arguments, excuses and evasions, he was telling me what we should take along, how long we would be gone, where the greatest views would be found.

"And when you get down there," he said, spreading his huge shoulders wider than ever, "please give my best to the folks at Phantom Ranch. You'll like them. And, oh man, what meals they serve! By the way, how much do you weigh?"

I told him, not knowing the object of the question.

"Oh, pshaw!" he ejaculated. "That makes you four pounds over the limit set for our mules!"

Jack looked deeply disappointed, but a wave of relief

swept over me. "Now isn't that too bad!" I said, my feeling belying my words. "Well, nice of you fellows to take such an interest in us and try to arrange everything. Maybe we'll be back in a few years and by that time I can reduce a bit. Thanks—guess we'll be going."

"Wait a minute, pardner," said Jack. "We won't let you be cheated out of that trip. I got an idea."

"Now, don't break any rules on my account," I protested. "I can see how you must set a load limit for those mules, and certainly I wouldn't abuse a mule."

"There are mules and mules," laughed Jack, his full confidence returning. "That load limit is made for our smaller mules that we like to use, because they are easier riding. But we have large mules for large parties. We can give you one of them. Now there is Z-Bar. Yes, sir, that's the one! Pardner, you're going to ride Z-Bar, smartest mule on the staff—and the biggest!"

Before I knew what was happening, I was carried into completing arrangements for that jiggling journey to the bottom of the Canyon! I had the feeling of being adrift in a boat with no oars, just going along with the current toward the brink of a roaring waterfall.

"Why not go tomorrow?" suggested Jack, now thoroughly triumphant. "The weather's perfect and ought to hold out for a few days."

"Oh, I don't believe Giny could get ready," I said weakly.

"Oh, yes, I could!" she insisted, in spite of the fact that I stepped on her toe.

"Fine! Fine!" said Jack, rubbing his great hands, and

right at that moment I thought what a splendid execu-
tioner he would make. "You folks be at the corral at
seven in the morning, and we'll have everything ready for
you—mules, guide and all."

"Why are you so determined to photograph the sunset
tonight?" asked Giny as we stood watching the changing
colors in the western sky. "We have more packing to
do, and there will be other sunsets."

"No, I want to record this one," I said determinedly.
"It may be the last one I'll ever see."

XVI

THROUGH THE AGES ON A MULE

I AWAKENED at dawn hoping it would all prove to be a dream—but it wasn't!

We were actually going on that mule trip into the Canyon. That which I had most feared had come upon me, like Job of old.

We arrived at the corral at the appointed hour. The men were already on hand and had the mules organized. Jack was there, whistling merrily, beaming with happiness over my demise. He introduced us to our guide, a tall boy named Pete, of mixed Mexican and American ancestry. Going into the Canyon via mulemobile was commonplace with him, and he was calloused beyond all enthusiasm and cordiality.

"This is your mule, Giny," Jack said, leading up a moderate-sized critter with a gray hide and stubborn face. "His name is Jeff. Just call him by name, tell him what you want him to do, and if he wants to, he'll do it. That is, I guess he would, but he has never wanted to do anything he was told so far."

"Jeff and I will get along all right," said Giny, patting the tough sides of the creature.

"And is this mine—is this Z-Bar?" I asked, pointing to another mule of about the same size that stood saddled.

"No—oh, no," Jack replied emphatically. "That is

152

Rosey. Pete will ride her. Here comes Z-Bar now. You can always identify him by that *Z* and a bar branded on his flank."

I looked toward the gate through which Z-Bar was entering, led by a cowboy. One glance and I knew I would never need to look at that mule's flank in order to identify him. I never saw such an animal before. I don't see how they got him all in one hide.

"Jack!" I exclaimed. "Are you sure that is just one mule?"

Jack nodded and laughed. "Z-Bar is lots of mule, lots of mule," he commented as he tightened up the cinch straps on Jeff.

"Are you sure it is a mule?" I asked in amazement. "If he had a trunk, he would make a wonderful elephant."

Z-Bar looked about the size and somewhat the shape of a grand piano. Already my knees and ankles began to ache as I thought of shaping my short legs around his bulging sides.

Giny was in her saddle now, looking annoyingly happy. Then I got aboard Z-Bar. I never have found out just how this was accomplished. I walked up to the huge animal in a sort of daze. I found the stirrup dangling somewhere in the region of my nose. There was no rope ladder nor elevator, and Z-Bar seemed not in the least inclined to kneel down as a camel might do, so I stood there helplessly. Then the boys of the corral closed in on me. Jack came up on my right side, looking energetic and powerful. Peter came up on the other, rolling up his sleeves.

Three Indian boys walked up behind me, and there were at least two others though I did not get a good look at them. They all took hold of me, and I had the sensation of being tossed in a blanket. When my senses steadied again I found I was sitting astride of Z-Bar—and I had learned to do the splits in one lesson!

My legs were sticking straight out at the sides, toes pointed forward like those hooks they have on mail cars. Even Z-Bar looked around incredulously and then turned loose an insulting strain of mule derisions. As to my sensations, no doubt they were something akin to those suffered on the racks of the Inquisition.

I learned to admire the self-control of both Pete and Jack during those few moments. They must have wanted to laugh, but they didn't. Both of them backed up a little, holding their chins and looking at me as if they couldn't believe the testimony of their eyes.

Jack was beside Z-Bar now, having regained his composure, and he said, "Mr. Campbell, you know that your feet ought to be in those stirrups, don't you?" I tilted over to one side and looked down at a stirrup. There were fully two feet between the position my foot held out in the air and that thing in which it was supposed to reside. I just looked at Jack helplessly and shook my head.

"Oh, you can do it!" he said with typical Western confidence. "Here, I'll help you."

Taking hold of my leg with his great big hands, he bent it around the sausagelike contour of Z-Bar, and forced my toe into the stirrup. Pete caught the atrocious idea and performed a like contortion on the other leg.

There I sat helplessly handcuffed, or footcuffed, to a mule. Giny and Jeff started to walk away, but I called to her, "Don't leave me now. If no one helps me off this thing I'll be here for the rest of my natural life!"

Jack seemed well satisfied at seeing me in this helpless position, and he gave the word for us to start our journey. Pete mounted his mule Rosey and we were off. From the corral it is only a short distance to the rim of the canyon where the trail turns abruptly down.

No words could ever describe my feelings when we began this steep descent. I could look right between Z-Bar's ears and see the bottom of the Canyon, nearly a mile below. If that mule had been equipped with brakes, I would have burned them out in the first 100 yards. By means of switchbacks, the Kaibab Trail, as it is called, goes down a wall as vertical as the side of a building. I was impressed with the appalling waste of labor in building this trail. It is eight to ten feet wide— but the mules use only the outside six inches! Z-Bar was passionately fond of flowers—not to see, but to eat. Whenever he found one growing on the outside of the trail, he would reach out and nip it off, while I held on to the saddle horn until my fingerprints were permanently registered thereon!

"Before us lies the Grand Canyon of the Colorado River." Pete began a memorized speech prepared for regular tourist trade. Z-Bar let out a snort as much as to say, *Do I have to listen to that again?* "We shall descend over a mile, and there find the great, roaring Colorado awaiting us. . . . *Giddap!*"

"Lucky River," I commented, my voice gauged for the limit of Z-Bar. "At least it didn't have to go down on a mule."

"We are now passing through the layer of rock known as the—wha-cha-call-it?—Kaibab limestone," orated Pete, his voice strengthened by pride of knowledge. "This rock has—that is, funny doodads in it that look like corals, sponges and shark's teeth. The layer is 550 feet thick."

"Ouch," I groaned, "only 550 feet down, so there are still nearly 5,000 feet to go!"

Z-Bar tossed his head and looked back at me as much as to say, *Listen, brother, don't do all the complaining. Remember, you're no cream puff to carry!*

Z-Bar was learning some things about me, I could tell by his behavior. Pete had given me certain instructions about handling him. "He's smart," said our guide. "Let him know he can boss you and he'll do it. Use your whip, beat him hard, he expects that and you can't hit hard enough to really hurt." But I couldn't lash that interesting old mule, who hadn't done anything to me. He knew it, all right. Presently he wouldn't do anything I asked him to.

In helplessness I became philosophical about the whole affair. I reached up and got hold of one of Z-Bar's big ears. "Listen, Z-Bar," I said, "it's all your show now. You go where you want to, when you want to, and you may be sure I'll come along." Actually Z-Bar seemed to behave better after that.

"This is the Coconino sandstone," lectured Pete. "Notice it is a different color. (Step up there, Jeff! Come on

Z-Bar!) The grain of this rock looks like wind-blown sand which was piled up in dunes (What's the matter with you, Rosey!), and sometimes you find (Rosey!) marks that look like some strange critter's been walking around it. This layer is 300 feet thick—I think!"

"That's 850 feet to this point, Z-Bar," I murmured. "Still over 4,000 to go."

"Now we are entering the Hermit Shale layer. (Rosey!)" Pete jerked the mule's head away from a nibble at some wayside grass. "This rock looks like river mud, contains many impression of (Jeff, you lousy critter, come on here!) ferns, plants, wings, doodads and stuff. This deposit is 300 feet thick, just like t'other'n."

While listening to Pete's running narration, I was watching Z-Bar and the other mules and developing an appreciation of them. They certainly were trailwise. How carefully they selected their footing! Their steps were so designed and directed that the weight was never put on an advancing foot until the mule was sure that it was well placed. When Pete occasionally declared a rest period, the mules would turn crosswise of the trial, heads to the outside, for greater safety and comfort.

"Now we are entering the Supai formation, 'bout eight foot thick," droned Pete, mixing in some cowboy words with memorized lines and launching out oratorical gestures that made Rosey toss her head. "I mean 800 feet thick. (Rosey, plague take your thick hide, you got me all muddled up!) It is sandstone, limestone and shale, and has a lotta—er—funny stuff and marks in it. Note—" he pointed dramatically—"the difference in the color of the rocks we have come through. They got something in 'em that does that. At the lower edge of the Supai formation we are 2,000 feet below the rim."

"Z-Bar," I whispered, "I believe I am going to make it. *Ouch!* Don't do that again or you are going to finish this alone." Z-Bar had slipped, jolting me and sending a pain from the tip of my big toe to the roots of my hair.

Mixing mule griping with scientific dissertation, Pete talked all the way to the bottom of that first descent. While we passed through the famous switchbacks of the Redwall, a deposit of red limestone 500 feet thick, he had trouble with Z-Bar. Z-Bar had found some sort of shrub that suited his palate, and all the jerking, pulling and pleading I could do didn't make him budge. Pete called to him, but no response. Then Pete rode back past Giny and her Jeff, intent on giving Z-Bar a sound lacing. Z-Bar watched him coming and continued eating until Pete was within a few feet, then he voluntarily ceased his lunch and walked on. Pete was entirely defeated. He couldn't whip Z-Bar then, so he contented himself with telling the mule some most uncomplimentary things about himself. Z-Bar put his ears back so he couldn't hear and walked on.

Down and down we went through the clearly marked layers of Muav limestone, Bright Angel shale and Tapeats sandstone. We paused to rest the mules in view of the impressive Roaring Springs, where a gushing waterfall comes spurting right out of the rocky side of the Canyon, the waters forming the famous Bright Angel Creek so often mentioned in the early history of the region.

At noon we stopped for lunch at Ribbon Falls. Here one lone cottonwood tree offered some shelter from the blazing sun. Heat is a part of the traveler's difficulty in the Grand Canyon. It is desert country down there, and the sun beats down unmercifully.

Our steep descent was now over. There was a long ride ahead of us, but it was relatively level travel. We went through Bright Angel Canyon, crossing and recrossing the clear-watered stream. The course of the Bright Angel Creek follows a great crack thought to be created by an earthquake long, long ago. As the day was coming to a close we neared Phantom Ranch, the end of our journey.

"We have now reached the bottom of the Canyon," orated Pete, putting a poetic finale to his narration. "Half mile on is the Colorado, singing its ancient song. It sang there before Columbus discovered America, it sang before—er—Cannibal crossed the Alps, it sang——"

"Needle must have got stuck in a groove," I whispered to Z-Bar. "I feel as if I have been in the saddle longer than that." Z-Bar shook his head as if to say, Me too! Pete's concluding lines were lost in giggles which Giny could not control.

We shall not forget our reception at Phantom Ranch. Jack Burns was right; these were mighty fine folks! They came out to meet us, reaching up to shake hands and making us feel important and welcome. Then they helped us off our mules. At least, they told me I was off the mule. I could hardly believe it, for I felt just the same as I had on Z-Bar's back. My legs retained their new-found shapes, and I looked like the first arch on a croquet set.

Mostly under the influence of his own oratory, Pete had warmed up to us now. He seemed actually solicitous. "Mr. Campbell," he said, as I stood there trying to convince myself that I was actually standing on the ground, "I would suggest that you don't try to walk right away."

"Pete!" I returned. "Put your mind at rest. I couldn't take a step if you pushed me. You go on and do all your chores, and when you want to find me, I'll be standing right here."

Giny was moving around making the marvelous discovery that she could still walk. Finally a shower bath and a swim in the pool formed of the waters of Bright Angel Creek helped bring us back to normal. We were quartered in a lovely little cabin where we could see the south rim of the Grand Canyon towering over us, and hear the endless song of Angel Creek as it made its way to the Colorado River a half mile beyond.

Presently the dinner bell rang. Such wonderful food, served in such a hospitable way! We felt as if we had known these people always and were guests in their home. It was one of the grandest meals I had ever sat down to, and the marvel was that I could.

XVII

DOWN IN HEAVEN

DINNER now a most happy memory, Giny and I walked out into the cool gloom of early evening. We have known and loved the peace of this magic hour in many of nature's mansions—in the lake-studded forests of the north, high in the mountains of the West, in treeless plains and in measureless deserts—but it seemed to us at the moment that none of them could match the heavenly quiet that reigned at the bottom of Grand Canyon.

"I am reluctant to say it," I confessed to Giny, "but this is worth all the jolts, joggles and contortions I went through to get here!"

We walked by the corral. There we could see Z-Bar towering above companion mules, their heads close together, apparently talking over events of the day. Z-Bar discovered us and pointed our way with his big ears, as if saying, *There he is now. Can you imagine carrying THAT down from the north rim? You fellows were lucky.*

We sauntered on down the Kaibab Trail, which at this point follows the course of Bright Angel Creek to the Colorado River. Above us towered the walls through which the river had carved its way during countless ages. Faintly in the distance we could see the slender span which we knew to be the Kaibab Bridge. Over this the

Kaibab Trail began its assent of some eleven miles to the south rim. This bridge is a monument to human ingenuity and courage. Much of the material used in it was brought down by mule back—which makes the faithful, enduring animals heroes along with the men. The bridge is 440 feet long and is suspended seventy feet above the water.

The Colorado is more than a mere waterway. It is the visible symbol of unlimited power and inexhaustible purpose. It is time in liquid form, a fluid sculptor chiseling images of the ages. True, the Colorado is not beautiful, so far as its waters are concerned. The majestic cliffs through which it flows are colorful and impressive, but the river itself is red-brown with its ponderous load of silt. Its sand- and gravel-laden waters are still carving deeper into the earth. Every twenty-four hours they carry at least 1,000,000 tons of debris past any point of their winding course.

As we reached our cabin, we noted a circle of jolly, visiting folks outside the dining lodge. The lodge manager and his wife, the cook, the waitress, several guides, including Pete, and a government ranger were seated in comfortable camp chairs enjoying the light refreshing breeze that drifted down the Canyon.

"Come on, folks, here are some chairs," said the manager. "This is a nightly ceremony with us. The daytimes are pretty hot, and sitting out in this evening air is one of our greatest pleasures down here."

We were introduced to those whom we had not previously met, and in a matter of minutes all were talking as freely as if we had known one another for years.

Presently I sensed something touching my shoulder and felt warm breath on the back of my neck. I turned my head slowly—and looked right into the eyes of a beautiful antlered buck deer!

"Do you all see what I see?" I asked. "Is this real or stuffed?"

They laughed. "That is Mulligan and he's very real, though I think he wants to be stuffed," said the cook. She was a charming lady whom we learned to know simply as Mrs. Y. "He comes every night begging. Here—here is some whole-wheat bread I have waiting for him. You feed him."

Giny was on her feet now, talking to our beautiful visitor. While we fed him we learned Mulligan's story. He had been found in the forest when a fawn and was then in very poor condition. This was over three years ago. A ranger brought the creature to the lodge and Mrs. Y. took him under her care.

"You never saw a more heroic case of nursing in your life," commented the manager. "Mrs. Y. actually sat up nights with that fawn. The rest of us went on half-rations until Mulligan was on his feet."

"Oh, he's a darling," said Mrs. Y. "Mulligan, come here!" Mulligan walked away from us and our offer of more food and literally put his huge head in Mrs. Y.'s lap. He held perfectly still while she scratched back of his ears. "This is an old stunt of ours," said Mrs. Y. "Mulligan loves this, and so do I."

There were other shadowy forms coming out of the night now. Presently there were six deer in our circle, wandering from one guest to another for bites of food and petting. There were a doe with two fawns, one larger doe, a spikehorn buck and, of course, Mulligan, who continued to monopolize Mrs. Y.

Giny plucked at my sleeve. "What is that up in the tree looking down at us? It looks like the face of a raccoon."

"Oh, it's Mugsy," said the ranger. "Mugsy, the ring-tailed cat. Come down here, Mugsy!" And Mugsy did.

"Oh, you beautiful creature!" exclaimed Giny, fascinated by the lovely, quick-moving ringtail. "Come over to me, will you?"

"No," said the ranger, "he never comes to anyone except Mrs. Y., and not always to her. He runs all around us, but he won't let us touch him."

Mugsy had made his way down the tree and across the ground to a pan of food which had been left for him. His movements were wonderfully graceful and swift. He climbed the tree with the agility of a squirrel. His long slender body made him resemble a fox somewhat, though his tail with seven black stripes ended the similarity. The ringtail is closely related to the raccoon.

Mugsy was soon followed by members of his family. We now had six deer and four ringtails to watch. Giny and I were having a marvelous time.

"Why didn't someone tell me this was down here?" I asked. "I would have ridden Z-Bar down backwards to see this."

Peter laughed heartily. "Z-Bar might have something to say about that," he suggested.

Giny plucked my sleeve again and pointed back into

the darkness. By this time we were expecting almost anything to happen. Just at the limit of vision I could see a huge form moving toward us, so large it seemed a piece of the night itself had become animated. There was the sound of heavy hoofs. "Is something coming?" I asked Mrs. Y., "or am I seeing things?"

She looked toward the approaching form and then laughed. "That's Howard," she said. "It is about time for him to come. He has been gone all day. Come on, Howard!"

Howard came on, getting more huge at every step. He proved to be a mule larger than Z-Bar, if that were possible. He was built something along the lines of a dirigible balloon. There was no question as to his intentions. He walked unhesitatingly into the circle, pushing deer to one side and causing me to move quickly to keep from being tramped on as he went directly to Mrs. Y. "You big baby, you," she said, petting the mammoth head that reached into her lap. "Here is some cake I've been saving for you. Where have you been and what have you been doing?"

"You might as well accept Howard," commented the ranger. "He is as fixed in this Canyon as the Colorado River."

"From the corral?" I asked.

"No, Howard wouldn't stay in a corral. He won't stay any place, go any place, or do anything he's supposed to."

"A pack mule?"

"Howard work?" said the ranger, raising his eyebrows. "Don't be silly. Howard has retired. It was his own decision. He used to be used on the trail, but he organized himself into a one-mule union and went on strike. That was two years ago. He hasn't done a lick of work since."

Howard's story was a classic of animal decision. He wouldn't be harnessed and he wouldn't be ridden. No amount of argument or even severe whippings would change his mind in the least. His decision came suddenly. For years he was a most faithful animal, carrying on the hard work of the trail both as a saddle mule and pack animal. But that was over; he had struck for no work at all and better food. He was getting it.

"The other day I saw him down by the river," the ranger said. "Howard and I are right good friends, and I started to walk up to him, as I always do, to pet him I was surprised when he tossed his head and backed away from me. I talked to him, then tried again to approach him, but he would have nothing to do with me. Then I realized what was wrong. I had my riding boots on, and he was looking right at them. He thought I was going to ride him and he intended that it wasn't going to happen. Just to see if I was right, I went back to my cabin and put on another pair of shoes—lower, hiking shoes. When I came back, he walked right up to me. Mrs. Y., tell about the time he went in the kitchen."

"Oh!" Mrs. Y. peered around her mammoth pet. "Well, that really wasn't Howard's fault. He was influenced by Mulligan. You see, Mulligan lived in the house at one time, and he feels special privilege. He comes to the door, and we still let him in occasionally. He had learned how to open the screen door on the kitchen himself. He would paw at it until it opened, then in he would come. Well, Howard watched Mulligan do this stunt and he saw that Mulligan was always rewarded by some good food when he got inside. Once Mulligan went in when no one was around and he ate a whole blueberry pie I had just baked. Howard decided he was as clever as Mulligan, and one evening he walked up to the door and pawed at it. You didn't know your own strength, did you, honey?"

she said to the mule. "You just kicked the door off its hinges and walked in. It took all the king's men to get you out again, didn't it, pet?"

Howard went about the circle, accepting a bit of petting and a bite of food from each one. He paused skeptically in front of me. "These aren't riding boots, Howard," I assured him. "Anyway, I have had enough mule riding to last me a long time. Don't you be afraid." He let me pat him, but he kept an eye on my field boots just the same.

"Giny," I said when we had returned to our cabin and were about to enjoy a wonderful, restful sleep, "I have large ears, haven't I?"

She looked puzzled. "Well, I guess they are a little larger than the average. Why do you ask?"

"And I am just a little bit stubborn, sort of like a mule, am I not?"

"A little—now what is all this?"

"I am just trying to qualify myself."

"For what, pray tell."

"For membership in Howard's union! I'd like to stay here in the bottom of Grand Canyon the rest of my life, and that would be the only way I could do it!"

XVIII

TORNADOES BY MAIL

OUR stay at Phantom Ranch was timeless as the Canyon itself. Day after day of the lazy warmth and quiet lulled us into a languor that was all too pleasing. We slept late in the cool mornings, sauntered the trails at unhurried pace, rested in the shade of cottonwood trees, swam in the Ranch pool. In fact, Giny and I had a vacation experience which was a novelty in our busy lives.

It was lovely to be lazy, but our do-nothing period was broken up sharply. One day a ranger arrived, riding through from the north rim to the south rim. He inquired for the Campbells. "I have a message for you," he said. "An Indian named John Corn asked me to say this to you: 'I have found what you are looking for!' Does that mean anything to you?"

"Yes, I think I understand," I replied. "Thank you for bringing the message."

"I'm curious. What did you lose—a watch, billfold, or what?"

I laughed. "Nothing lost. John has located a picture I want, that is all."

After the ranger left, Giny asked what I made of the message.

"I believe John has found our mountain lion!" I declared. "We must leave in the morning."

We left early on our return journey to the north rim. Pete thought it wise to get through the Bright Angel Canyon stretch before the sun was high. Temperatures up to 130 degrees have been recorded in that canyon. The walls are high and close together, and when the sun concentrates on the place, it becomes literally an oven. By late morning we were well beyond the area of extreme heat. To our delight we learned that riding uphill on a mule is a more comfortable experience than riding down. You fit better in the saddle, and there isn't that constant resistance to the downward pitch that makes the leg muscles feel so abused.

Giny had an experience that was exciting while it lasted. We had reached the steep part of our climb, and Z-Bar was going slower than ever. Jeff and Rosey were several switchbacks ahead of him. In the brush at the trailside there was a sound which both Giny and Jeff heard. It may have been a snake—Giny wasn't sure. Jeff wasn't sure either and he was taking no chances. Raring up on his hind legs like a spirited show horse, he whirled around and started down the trial. Fortunately, Giny went right with him. She really is a natural rider. I saw the whole thing from about 100 feet below and managed to turn Z-Bar so he blocked the trail. It wasn't necessary, though, as Jeff recovered his composure and came to a full stop. Pete had dismounted and came like a monkey down the side of the mountain, landing in front of Jeff and catching hold of his bridle. It was all over in a minute's time. Jeff was not the least bit excited; he hadn't intended to run away, he just didn't want to be near that funny noise. For once Z-Bar walked at a decent pace, and we reached the scene of action. Pete and I searched for a snake, but could find none. It may have been only the tumbling of a rock or the flight of a small bird. Anyway, we were deeply grateful for the way it turned out.

The return journey naturally took longer than the trip down into the Canyon. Travel up the steep slopes was slow, and frequent rest periods for the mules were necessary. When at long last we arrived at the corral on the north rim, we were saddle-weary. There I did the meanest thing I have ever done to Giny. I took her picture as she got off Jeff and walked away. I wouldn't know just how to describe that walk. It was something like the waddle of a duck with bunions. One foot would start in a direction it wasn't supposed to go, and by a wide circling movement land in front of the other one. I hid the camera so my dismounting could not be registered, and thereby deprived the world of a classic in the ridiculous.

We had dinner served in our cabin that evening, so we could look into our mound of mail as we ate.

"Six letters from Hi-Bub," exclaimed Giny. "Something exciting must have happened."

Plenty had happened. We arranged the letters according to date of postmark so that we might read them in order. The first one began with an exclamation point.

Dear Giny and Sam:
  Zipper has disappeared!
  Zanie discovered it first. He came barking to our

cabin this morning before dawn. We couldn't make him be still. We followed him and he took us all around the island hunting everywhere. He kept whining all the time. We found Zinnia and Zowie, but Zipper was gone. She has been making little practice swims lately, and I guess finally decided she could make it to the mainland. Don't hang up, Tony and I are headed out to find her.

LATER. Zipper is back! Guess who found her. It was Bill! Zipper was nearly five miles away; came right up to a farm house. Bill happened by and recognized her by that rope scar that is still on the back of her neck.

Now we can eat our breakfast—forgot all about it.

Love,

Hi-Bub

"Oh, can't you just feel the excitement of those boys when that happened?" exclaimed Giny.

"Yes, and why do you suppose Zipper swam away?" I returned. "She isn't old enough to do that—or is she?"

"Apparently she is," said Giny logically. "Well, let's see what the second letter has to offer."

It was so full of excitement it nearly jumped out of the envelope.

Dear Giny and Sam:

Zipper has gone again! Zanie got us up in the middle of the night to tell us. The sun hasn't come up even now. We are waiting for it to get light, and then we go after her. It ought to be easier to find her this time for we put a red ribbon on her neck. Tony is getting some breakfast ready. We will leave in a few minutes.

LATER! Zinnia is missing too! Zanie wouldn't settle down. He kept whining and pleading with us. He led us to the shed where Zinnia sleeps, and she wasn't there.

We searched the island, but no skunk! What do we do now?

STILL LATER! We want a meal of venison—raw! We are so mad at Zipper we could pick her spots off one at a time. We scoured the country for her yesterday. No Zipper anywhere. We called until we were hoarse. Zanie hunted like the swell dog he is, sniffing every inch of this whole forest. No Zipper. We just returned footsore, weary, discouraged, downhearted, disappointed and some other things. THERE ON THE ISLAND RIGHT AT THE BACK DOOR, ACTING AS IF NOTHING HAD HAPPENED, STOOD ZIPPER! Little does she know how close she is to being fried alive.

Going after Zinnia tomorrow.

Love,
Hi-Bub and Tony

"Quick! Open the next letter," I begged Giny. "What is the news about Zinna?"

"It is postmarked two days after the other letter," she observed. "They must have been busy."

The third letter popped like a firecracker.

Dear Giny and Sam:

Help! Help! And quick! Hold this letter at arm's length and downwind from you. I hope nothing gets in it but the story I have to tell.

Yesterday we searched from morning to night for our skunk. We worked over the mainland until Tony and I know every tree and bush by its first name. No Zinnia.

Last night Tony thought he would make one more try before going to bed exhausted. He went over to the mainland and started looking around with a flashlight. He saw Zinnia and walked up to her. ONLY, IT WASN'T

ZINNIA! Whoever it was let him have it, and there was plenty of IT. He came back smelling worse than some kinds of politics. Where is he now? I have him buried back of the boathouse. Even Zanie, Zowie and Zipper won't have anything to do with him. Over long distance he dictated this masterpiece:

> There once was a funny bohunk
> Who searched for a cute little skunk;
> He found the polecat,
> And so that was that.
> Now his social standing is sunk.

> More later,
> Hi-Bub and Tony (by proxy)

"Poor Tony!" Giny and I burst out in unison. He would be the one to pick up a strange skunk. After all, skunks look alike, and there ought to be a law against it.

"The fourth letter came by special delivery," said Giny opening it as she spoke. "What do you suppose has happened now?" The boys wrote:

Dear Giny and Sam:

Where should I begin this? Well, let's talk about Tony first. When I sent the previous letter, he was buried —at least he should have been. I dug him up and started to reclaim him, though it seemed a waste of time. While I burned his clothes, he washed in kerosene, lemon juice, tomato juice, and some soap that smells worse than skunk perfume.

Right at the end of all this gruesome task, we discovered Zinnia on the island again. Only it wasn't just Zinnia, she was twins! She brought home a playmate, and Tony insists it is the same skunk that was so impolite to him. The two of them are feeding at Zinnia's pan right now, and Zanie is feeding with them.

LATER—MUCH LATER! Zanie's almost mad. He is sitting on the front step howling. Tony and I have decided to let him howl while we get some dinner. We haven't had a bite since breakfast and it is nine o'clock at night. Zanie came to us a little before noon so excited he nearly ran out of his own hide. We knew someone was missing, so we went with him. We found Zinnia and her pal, but Zipper and Zowie were both gone. Has anyone got a nice twelve-foot fence that we can put around the island? This feels like trying to hold an armful of eels. Tony and I have about decided that the thing to do is to let them go and come as they please, as if we had any choice in the matter. Zanie won't let us. He howls and barks whenever we quit looking and keeps it up until we join him. Now he can just howl his head off—we have to have something to eat.

STILL LATER! We thought it was awful quiet. Now we find Zanie has left the island! He's out looking for his pals. Here we go again. Hope we have good news for you in the next writing.

Love,
Hi-Bub and Tony (in person)

Letter number five was written forty-eight hours after the previous one. Zipper had been seen, Zanie came back, but nothing was known of the whereabouts of Zowie.

Letter number six was a flurry of excitement with an element of foreboding. It read:

Dear Giny and Sam:
This letter would be a book if I told all that has happened in the last few hours.
To begin with, Zipper came back in the middle of last

night, bringing two wild deer with her. We heard a splashing, and Zanie barked a little, so we took our flashlight and went out. Zipper was just coming out of the water onto the island, the other two following her. She walked up the bank toward us, and we spoke to her. The other two were standing in the shallow water. Zanie suddenly was carried away with enthusiasm. He raced up to Zipper and stood on his hind legs, licking her in the face. Then he began one of those wild runs of his, the way he does when he is extra happy. That was more than the wild deer could stand. They jumped into the lake and swam away. Zipper stayed on.

This morning Zowie came back. We are hoping he won't run into the new skunk. I have never seen an animal so nearly starved. He looked and acted as if he hadn't had a square meal since he left. We fed him all he would eat, and now he is asleep under the shed. Zanie was happy to see him, but the fox wouldn't play. He seemed to be all in, probably been running ever since he left the island.

NOW COMES THE BIG NEWS. We went to Somewhere Lake for the first time since the tornado struck here. The Seven Secrets were all over the place. Are they getting cute! We saw some brush sticking out of the lake at one place and believe they are beginning to make a food cache there. No evidence of a house as yet.

Tony and I walked around the lake to see how the cutting was going. There are twelve trees down, and twenty more show cuttings. One beaver cut a limb off while we watched him. Looks good for your pictures.

Just before we left came a surprise that is a little frightening. On the shore opposite the point where our trail begins, we found tracks made very recently by a *man!* Who is it that has cut in on our secret?

Love,
Hi-Bub and Company

Giny looked worried, and so did I. From the description, this visitor had come from the forest area beyond the lake and not over our trail. That meant that it was someone familiar with the woods. Our contemplations were interrupted by a knock at our door.

"John and Kona!" cried Giny as she opened it. "How glad we are to see you! Come in!"

It was a happy reunion. Kona ran and threw himself in Giny's arms. John extended his strong handshake to me.

"We were so disapopinted when we found your camp gone, John," I said. "You hadn't told us you were going away."

"It was a sudden decision," replied the Indian, smiling. "I guess I was just self-conscious. I thought I would never tell my story to anyone, and after I talked to you I wanted to get away. So, Kona and I went into a region I have always liked—to the west."

"We wished for you at the bottom of the Canyon," Giny managed to say in spite of a bear hug by Kona.

"Tell me—" John looked at me earnestly—"did you enjoy the trip down?"

"Not so much the trip down, my friend," I replied, rubbing myself where aches had been, "but being down there was wonderful!"

"You—go—down?" Kona risked his father's displeasure with one little tease.

"Yes, we went down!" I said between clinched teeth, shaking him in spite of Giny's protection. "We went down, we saw, and we were conquered. It is a wonderful place."

Our friends were seated, and we gave them a detailed account of our Canyon experience. They were especially interested in the story of the animals at Phantom Ranch. John had known Mulligan, the buck, the year the fawn had been brought in. Kona squealed with delight when his father repeated to him the story of Howard the mule and the cute ringtails.

"Another year, and I shall take Bohunk down there," said John. "He rides pretty well now, but he is so small the mule wouldn't know he was in the saddle. He'll be ready next year."

"Your message brought us out of the Canyon," I said. "Did I interpret it right that you have found a mountain lion?"

"*To'hoo!*" exclaimed Kona excitedly. "*To'hoo! To'hoo!*"

"Yes," said John, quieting his child. "We have seen *to'hoo,* the mountain lion. There is a female with two or three young not far from our camp sunning herself on the rocks each morning."

"Splendid!" I exclaimed. "What do we do now? Where and how do we go?"

"You have some camping equipment?" asked John.

"Yes."

"Could you go in the morning?"

"Yes."

"Very well," said the Indian. "We will take you to our camp. Better be prepared to spend a few days there. We have plenty of provisions. The only drawback is that you must ride in our old car. It is a bit rough but it will get you there. I have named it Mulo, the mule. We go over a fire lane that is not traveled more than once a year."

Kona didn't quite understand all that had happened. He spoke in Hopi and in rather a loud voice for him. Entwined in the other words I could make out *to'hoo,* so I knew the nature of his inquiry. His father said simply, *"Kabo."*

"Does *Kabo* mean tomorrow?" I asked, reasoning out the conversation. John nodded.

"Kabo to'hoo!" I said to Kona. *"Kabo to'hoo!"*

His eyes widened to hear me say words in his native tongue. Then he danced around repeating over and over again, *Kabo to'hoo*—tomorrow the mountain lion.

XIX

INDIAN WORLD

JOHN and Kona stayed at a neighboring cabin for the night. We had breakfast with them the next morning. Our table in the Lodge dining room was right before one of the huge picture windows through which we looked down into the Canyon.

Word had gone about the Lodge that we were back from our Canyon trip, and suddenly Giny and I found ourselves the center of attention. Our little waitress and the dining-room hostess came up with the greeting, "So, you came back!" Was it such a surprising thing that we did? The hotel manager approached the table and greeted us with "So, you came back!" Jack Burns walked the length of the dining room, spurs clicking every step, to say through a broad smile, "So, you came back!" I felt about ready for a Congressional Medal of Honor.

"Jack," I said, after assuring the admiring multitude that we *had* come back, "Giny and I have been noticing how much more friendly the Canyon seems now. We feel that we are part of it."

"I knew you would say that!" he exclaimed triumphantly. "Everyone who goes down the trail says he made friends with the Canyon on the trip. You see—" he brought his great hand down on my shoulder with such force I felt the shock down to my ankles—"you have been initiated." I was sure I knew what he meant! "You are no longer a tenderfoot and a visitor—you have joined the Canyon Fraternity. You're one of us, my friend," he affirmed. "You'll never get away from us now."

"We don't want to get away," commented Giny. "Sam and I will have to see this country regularly, and we are going down again, aren't we, dear?"

I nodded my head, but secretly I was glad the next trip was in the distant future.

"Our friends, John and Kona, are taking us into the back country today," I informed him.

"Good!" said Jack. "No one knows the country better than he. Where to, John?"

John named the area into which we were going.

"Oh, oh," said Jack, raising his eyebrows. "That is wild country. Reckon no one has been out there for a year or more. Going on the old fire lane?"

"Yes."

"Hope you make it. By the time you get there, you'll think vou have had another ride on Z-Bar."

Between conversations, we finished our breakfast and then went about final preparations for our next adventure.

A wire was dispatched to Hi-Bub and Tony reading,

Your letters awaiting us when we came out of Canyon. Glad life is not monotonous back there. Don't worry about animals—just be careful not to get lost yourselves. Will write in a few days. Love, Giny and Sam.

The journey to the Indian's camp was all that Jack had said it would be. I think I know now how it would feel to be a pebble inside a baby's rattle. It was the first time I had ever followed a blazed trail by automobile. The fire lane on which we started had some resemblance to a road in its early stages, but soon this disappeared and John was driving by marks on trees. The ground was hard but rough and uneven. Mulo was a miracle of endurance. "What-wut ki-yind of a k-war is this?" I asked, as I shuttled between the seat and the car top.

"Made it myself out of spare parts," answered John, a little more steady in his position back of the wheel. "I call it a Hopi Special, meaning we hopi we get where we are going."

"Whee-e-e-e!" yelled Kona, who was having the time of his life. He and Giny were in the back seat where it was rougher, if possible, than where John and I sat. He said something that provoked John to answer, *"Kaeh!* (no) you Bohunk!" Then to me: "Do you know what he says? He wants me to find bigger bumps to go over—this is too smooth for him."

"Whee-e-e-e!" cried Kona, as we went over a log.

Mulo, the Hopi Special, held together until we reached the Indian's camp late in the afternoon. Two fenders were waving and rattling furiously for the last few miles, but John said he could tighten them.

The camp was in a grove of beautiful aspens— *tuvwo'bi,* Kona and John called these graceful trees. The Indian's tent was pitched in the shelter of a high rock, and near them they had cleared a place for ours. One hundred yards away was the edge of a canyon, a tributary to the Grand Canyon. Down a short way on a trail was a fine spring, the source of the camp water supply.

As we began putting up our tent, Kona went wild with joy. John explained that he was always happy when they camped in faraway places, and now that Giny and I were to camp there too, he was out of control. In fact, he was a precious nuisance. Every move I tried to make, he was right in the way. John put him aside a dozen times, gave him tasks invented to keep him busy—he even put him up in a tree—but each time he was back under foot in less than a minute. He had learned to say our names, or at least words that sounded something like them. We had to convince John that we did not consider it discourteous in the least, and then Kona was allowed to call us "Gina" and "Saum"—which was as near as he could get them.

Presently the youngster came toward me, crawling on his hands and knees, saying, "Saum, *honani! Gr-r-r, honani!*"

"Oh," said John, as I looked to him for explanation. "He is *honani,* the badger."

He was positively delighted when he heard Giny and me call him *Honani.* In fact, whenever we learned and used a Hopi word, a regular gusher of giggles came from the boy. Since we liked to hear him giggle, our Hopi vocabulary was constantly on the increase. Now he came hopping along and he was *tavu* the rabbit. Alternately he became *ho'nauuh* the bear, *le'taigo* the gray fox, *puchah* the skunk, *panwu* the mountain sheep, *tukya* the prairie dog, and *munyauwu* the porcupine. Once we had learned the names, he tested us by imitating the animal and we were supposed to tell him what it was. John helped us a little, so we got along fairly well. It was sufficient reward to hear Kona's outburst of delight when we got it right.

In spite of Kona we got our tent in order. That is the first rule of good camping, to make ready for the night. Giny and John co-operated in getting dinner ready, and Kona and I walked down to the canyon rim to look at the sunset. "Saum," he said, tugging at my hand and pointing to the west, *"Tawa."*

"Tawa," I repeated, understanding it to mean sunset. He laughed delightedly.

"Saum," he said again, pointing overhead, *"Kachi!"*

I noted he was indicating the new moon, now sharply outlined in the darkening sky. *"Kachi,"* I said, and Kona said, "Whee-e-e," which is the same in any language. Later I learned that this word means not just moon, but refers to a crescent moon on its back.

Our dinner was a good one. Afterward, at Giny's special request, we had an evening campfire. Kona helped us identify voices of *isava* the coyote, *zrana* the little frog that calls constantly, *monvu* the owl, and *toko'chi* the wildcat. At last he settled in Giny's arms. It had been a busy day for such a little man. Presently he was in the land of dreams.

John sat looking through the night toward the Canyon. The afterglow persisted in the western sky, cradling the young moon and sending a mellow light across the landscape that gave indistinct outline to distant formations. Tenuous mists, born of the chill evening air, rendered that filmy, shadowy effect which savors of dreams and legends.

Giny and I spoke in low voice of the beauty about us,

but John entered not into our conversation and indeed seemed not to hear us. In the red glow of the campfire he presented a picture which will remain in our memory. His eyes became wide, staring, and fixed as though he were penetrating the veil of appearances and looking into some distant realm and remote time. For many minutes he moved not a muscle, nor did he respond to the occasional remarks addressed to him.

Presently he began a low chant, which Giny said later sent little chills down her spine. Not that the chant was frightening, but rather that there was an eerie feeling of mystery to it all. John's voice increased in tone and his hands moved to the rhythm of his singing. *"Si-ai, a-hai, si-ai, a-hai,"* he chanted on and on.

"A Hopi song to the night, John?" I asked, speaking loudly to get his attention.

He looked up at us startled. For a moment there was no recognition in his eyes. He had been completely carried away with his own meditations and was dwelling in a thought world quite apart from us. When he realized what he had done he smiled, quite embarrassed, and said, "I'm sorry. I was dreaming, I guess. What did you ask?"

"Was your chant a Hopi song to the night?" I repeated.

"No, it is an ancient builder's song, the *kitdauwi* or house song," he said, quite in possession of himself again.

"Tell us of it, John." Giny was always seeking such pearls of legend and tradition. "Was it used by your people?"

"Yes—long, long ago, and it is still used today," replied John. "It began so long ago that no one now knows what the words mean. We know only that they are traditionally associated with the foundation of a home. No doubt that song was sung long before the white man came to America, when the Hopi lived on the lower range of plains far to the south." John made a sweeping gesture with his arm that aptly described the flat desert areas where the explorer Coronado and his men found the Hopi nation about 1540.

Giny would have asked another question, but I signaled her to look at John. The Indian was still swinging his arm back and forth as if stroking the desert home of his people.

"Sometimes I wish I had been born in those pre-white-man days," he was saying. "It is the primitive freedom for which I yearn, that which reigned in the days when my forefathers lived, faced only with the problems of nature. Living was fair and honest then. There is no deceit in nature, no prejudice. My people raised crops out of that desert soil. They learned the secrets of storing grain and other foods. They wove cloth out of native, desert cotton, they made baskets of grass and pottery of clay. They built dwellings of stone, logs and mud. Seven cities, or *pueblos* as you call them, did they build in the desert.

"It was a difficult life, but a good one. The people became strong and enduring. The young men could run from the time the sun came up until it set again. Older folks could work endless hours in the fields. They were peaceful, happy people. Many were their songs. They sang as they plowed and planted, sang as they wove, sang as they ground corn kernels between rocks—everything was done to song. When a builder was making his home he first sprinkled *piki,* or food crumbs, on the ground where the walls were to stand, and as he did he sang,

'*Si-ai, a-hai, si-ai, a-hai,*' again and again. It was asking a blessing on his home."

"Your people had no wars?" asked Giny.

"Very few—until the white man came, seeking gold. Before them my people fled, deserting their cities and building seven new ones on the high mesas. There they live today, and there the house song can still be heard."

John was quiet for a moment. The slumbering Kona spoke several little Hopi words, moved to a more comfortable position in Giny's arms and continued his sleep. John looked at him adoringly. "I guess I dream too much with my eyes open," he said, smiling. "In fancy I wander those old desert lands, and sometimes it seems very real. I sit about the old council fires, work at the crops and weaving. Then I plan a home. I lay cornerstones as my people did hundreds of years ago. I take *piki,* and chant as I sprinkle it on the ground exactly where the walls of my home shall be. I build my home always for Kona and me—and Polimana."

He had risen to his feet now and stood looking down at me. I returned his smile and waited for him to speak the thoughts that showed in his eyes. "You lead me to talk," he said, laughing softly. "I do not understand it, but I guess it is because you can be trusted, you do not laugh at me. You are *Ikwa'chi,* my friend."

I did not answer by word, but reached my hand toward him. He grasped it strongly, then turned sharply away and walked out into the night toward the rim of the canyon. It was a long time before he came back, wearing a weary smile, and said simply, "I must put Kona to bed."

XX

CATS AND CALAMITIES

IT WAS raining the first morning at the Indian's camp. Our plans had been to rise at dawn and go down the trail to the place where John and Kona had seen the mountain lion. But when the early hour came we awakened to hear the soft, soothing patter of a light shower on our tent. We were lulled back to sleep and did not awaken again until well into the morning.

Then it was the scent of breakfast in preparation that was the alarm clock! We were quickly dressed and out of our tent. A pleasing sight met our gaze. Kona was putting some wood on the fire; John was busy brewing, frying and toasting various things over the flames. The sky had cleared and the sun was sending long silvery shafts through the veil of chill moisture that hung in the dripping forest.

"Top of the morning!" I called as I stepped out.

"Ah, *Ikwa'chi,* my friend," responded John. "You are up at last. Breakfast is nearly ready."

"Saum, Gina!" cried Kona, dropping his wood and running toward me, *"Lanaka! Lanaka!"*

"Now what in the world is that?" I asked. "Some new kind of animal?"

"It is *lanaka* the rainbow," called John. "There is a beautiful one hanging over the canyon."

The excited Kona led Giny and me out beyond the trees

where, in the western sky, we could see the heavens arched with a brilliant semicircular rainbow. A background for its colorful beauty was the dark cloud which had supplied the early-morning shower. Forked lightning completed the grand display, staged to the accompaniment of thunder echoing through the canyon caverns. The scene was too appealing to be denied, and breakfast waited while we brought our camera to bear on it.

Now Giny made a discovery which delayed the meal further. "John, you have been painting!" she exclaimed, indicating his easel set up in the shelter of a small tarpaulin. "Sam, come and see what this man is doing!"

We looked upon a painting of a cougar and three cubs sunning themselves on a shelf of rock. It seemed excellently done to me, and I was most enthusiastic. "John, this is splendid!" I exclaimed. "Will you sell this one to me?"

John laughed. "It isn't finished yet," he said. "If I ever feel convinced it is the painting you want, then you may have it."

"What must I do to convince you?"

"I think I shall know," he said, turning to the flat rock which served as a table. "Come, our cakes are getting cold."

That morning we explored the environment of the camp. We found most interesting neighbors. There was a family of white-tailed squirrels in a tree within a hundred yards of our tents. Saucy chipmunks darted across the forest floor. Bears had torn several logs apart to get the grub worms, showing that we had these great, interesting creatures near at hand. A waddling old porcupine climbed a tree as we came into his neighborhood. At a muddy spot we found tracks of a coyote and deer.

During the afternoon we went down the trail where *to'hoo,* the mountain lion, had been seen. It was a hazardous journey which seemed easy enough for John and Kona, but gave Giny and me plenty to think about. The trail was narrow, hovering near the brink of a steep slope. It would have been difficult enough for me without my camera, but with this awkward contraption and the responsibility it involves, I had my troubles.

After traveling about a quarter mile down the trail, John led us along a narrow ledge several hundred yards to one side. Coming up behind a huge rock outcropping, he motioned us to be still while he cautiously peeked around the outer edge. After looking into the distance for a moment, he abandoned caution and said aloud, "No, she is not there."

He pointed out the place where the big cat was usually seen, a ledge of rock on the opposite side of the narrow canyon. "She usually lies on that flat place," said John, "her kittens playing about just below her. The afternoon shadows are over the spot already, so I am sure it will be only morning hours in which we find her there."

He explained that he had made a sketch record from this very place, and from this was completing his painting.

"It is perfect for photography," I observed. "Shooting from here with the six-inch lens will take her in beautifully."

"Just be careful not to slip," warned John. "You wouldn't go far down, but it would be a bit rough. Anyway, you might frighten her out of the country. Let's get back early in the morning."

However, the next morning it was raining again, and we held closely to our tents. Through the day the rain continued, and a cold damp wind made us don all our woolen wraps. Toward evening the solid black cloud that had covered the sky all day long broke at the horizon, and the sun peered through the widening slit. The undersurface of the cloud turned blood-red, and the trees glistened with countless diamonds formed of dangling raindrops. "Be ready in the morning," commented John. "This means it will be clear. *To'hoo* will surely be there. Likely she has been living constantly in a damp cave and she will be wanting the sun."

"*To'hoo?*" questioned Kona.

"*Kabo*—tomorrow," answered his father.

"Whee-e-e-e!" squealed Kona.

The descent of the trail called for unusual caution that morning. Many minor landslides had been caused by the rain of the past two days. As we approached the great rock from which our observation was to be made, I had a sensation creep over me that was closely akin to the one occasioned by the antlered Prince of Cape Royal. "Giny," I whispered, "will you take observations with the range finder and exposure meter. Let's make sure we do everything just right. If *to'hoo* is there, this is the climax of our Western trip. Continually take light readings and distance measurements. I'll just work with the camera, and then I won't have to divide my attention."

"All right," she whispered back, her eyes dancing with excitement. "Give me the meter now, and I am ready."

John had given instructions to Kona, and the little Indian now stood like a tiny statue, the dignity, poise and composure of his race written in his happy face. There was no rushing about, no excited squealing. John moved silently to the outer end of the rock and looked toward the haunt of the big cat. "She is there!" he whispered. "Come with your camera. We will stand back."

"First get me the readings, Giny," I called, noticing a familiar tremble in my legs. "What exposure, what distance?"

"F. 8 at twenty-four frames per second," whispered Giny, studying her meter. She was peering around the rock, thrilled at the sight before her. "Oh, wait till you see what I see!" she commented. For such was our position that only one at a time could be at the viewpoint.

"Yes, yes!" I whispered a little impatiently, "but what I want to know is how much does she weigh?"

"How much does she weigh?" Giny looked puzzled. "How should I know how much she weighs?"

"Who said anything about her weight?"

"You did."

"I didn't—I want to know how far away she is."

"Listen here, young man," she said earnestly, "don't you break out with buck fever again. Is that what's the matter with you?"

"No, no, I am as calm as can be," I insisted. "Now what is the distance?"

"Sixty-five feet exactly," declared Giny, carefully studying the range finder.

I set my camera carefully. "Everything checks," I said. "Now let me shoot."

I carefully set up the camera at the edge of the rock. A most stirring sight met my gaze. There was *to'hoo* lying full length on the rock, looking like an overgrown house cat. About her played three cunning kittens. It would be difficult to imagine a more tranquil scene. The kittens showed no fear of their powerful mother at all, and when their play required it they ran right over her, even pausing for a fight on her neck and face. As a punishment she caught one of them with her great paw and held him while she washed his face thoroughly.

"F. 8 at twenty-four frames, distance sixty-five feet," I kept repeating to myself, and I checked these adjustments on my camera at least a dozen times.

The light was perfect, the beautiful animals filled the entire view finder, everything was beyond my fondest hopes. Here was the culmination of months of planning and endless dreaming! Here was the picture everyone thought I could never get!

Complimenting myself on the thoroughness with which I was conducting the whole procedure, I continued to shoot film. *To'hoo* stood up and stretched, and I got it. A little one tumbled head over heels down to a lower ledge; the mother jumped down with marvelous grace and ease, picked up the youngster and brought him back. I got it! The huge female once rolled over on her back and boxed with a kitten who reached down from a rock just above. I got it!

While I retreated back of the rock to change films in the camera, Giny, Kona and John took turns observing the family. "They are just precious!" exclaimed Giny in a whisper. "I never saw anything so wonderful before."

On my request she took another reading. It was the same, but I wanted everything to be just right. I shot another full reel of film, changed and shot yet another.

One most impressive incident was when the mother cougar became suddenly imbued with the play of her young. They were putting on a wild chase and fight, when she caught the spirit and executed the silliest jumps and queer antics. I got it all!

A photographer can never be satisfied, however. Wanting a little different camera angle, I decided to chance a move farther around the face of the big rock. As I took the first step a stone which looked solid enough gave way under me, and down the face of the cliff I went. Thinking mostly of the welfare of the camera, I held it high with my left hand, while I sailed along with a young avalanche of loose dirt and stones, leaving little samples of clothing and skin along the way. It was a terrific commotion, and the mountain-lion family went bounding up the face of the cliff, the mother leading the way and the youngsters following with marvelous agility. I didn't get that!

"Is everything all right?" called Giny, looking down at me where I had come to rest on the next ledge.

"Everything that is important," I called reassuringly. "I may have to borrow a pair of John's breeches and grow some new skin, but the camera wasn't touched!"

John was scrambling down to me, and Kona was calling something that I finally learned meant, "Please do it again!" John took the camera from me to lighten my troubles and led the way back. "Mighty glad you got your pictures first," he commented. "It is my guess that *to'hoo* will leave the country after being frightened that way. Well, you have your film, and I have my painting— so I guess we have much to be grateful for."

But I did not answer John. My eyes were fastened on the camera, and what I saw caused me to feel cold and numb.

"Giny!" I said as we reached the upper level, and she came to me. "Giny! Will you please push me off the cliff?"

"Will I what?"

"Push me off the cliff! Or, if you prefer, run and get a gun and gently shoot me at least six times?"

"What are you talking about?"

"Giny! Look at the camera, look closely at it."

"We-ell," she said, still puzzled. "You did a wonderful job of protecting it in that fall, it isn't hurt in the ..."

Then she stopped short. "Sam! No, you couldn't have done that! You couldn't!"

But I had just the same. The cap had been on the lens all during the morning shooting, and all the film I had run would be totally blank!

"John," said Giny, "would you get me a gun with six nice soft bullets?"

"I'll be happy to," said John, who now understood.

XXI

HOMING INSTINCT

I HAVE heard the expression "in the dog house," but it doesn't begin to tell my situation after my tragedy of the camera and mountain lion. No puppy would have let me in. I was consigned to the habitat of *puchah,* the skunk, and not very welcome even there.

John was tireless in his efforts to redeem my cougar photography from utter failure. He made repeated visits to the rock where the cats had been seen, but they did not return. Leaving Kona with us so that his travel could be swift, he embarked on a day-long journey around the canyon to come up on the opposite side at the very site of the cougars' sunning place. Nowhere could he find evidence of their presence.

For four days this search continued. I photographed bear, deer and a funny old owl (with the lens cap OFF), but the opportunity of the cougars was the kind that knocks only once. We realized it was unwise to stay longer, for although it was a joy to live in this camp, we had much work to do and the summer was drawing to a close.

"Now, can I convince you that I really want that mountain-lion painting?" I asked John on the day set for our return to the Lodge. "Owning it would be the only consolation I could have after what has happened."

"All right," laughed John. "I am convinced that you want it. And certainly I want you to have it."

We succeeded in buying three of his canvases at a figure that seemed ridiculously low to us, but it was all John would accept. "It is the price I ask of others," he explained. "And what you and Giny have done for Kona and me is beyond estimate."

"Better that we add something for what you and Kona have done for us!" broke in Giny, drawing the youngster to her. "There is a corner in our hearts that will always belong to our little chipmunk."

Kona was looking up at Giny with a pained expression on his round, bronze face. *"Hakami'i?"* he asked in a soft voice, *"Hakami'i?"*

We looked to John for explanation. *"Hakami'i*—it means' where do you go?' " he said. "He sees you getting ready to leave and I haven't explained it to him."

He knelt before the boy and talked earnestly with him. Kona was close to tears at first, but gained control of himself and presently whispered his soft *"wi"* (yes).

"We would like to do our farewell song for you if you don't mind," said John, looking up at us. "We always bid farewell to our friends, whether people, animals, things or places."

"We would love it," said Giny.

Assuming their usual position, John on his knees, Kona standing before him, both facing us, they began a chant. The rhythm, the earnestness of the two Indians, the way they were caught up in the meaning of their song—all was most impressive.

"And now may we have our interpretation?" asked Giny when the ceremony was finished.

John thought for a moment, and then gave this English version:

> "Softly, softly the Great Spirit whispers—
> Whispers his words of great wisdom.
> Obediently we follow his commands.
> We greet you, O land before us!
> Be filled with the Great Spirit.
> Be joyful O land we are leaving,
> For the Great One dwells here too."

Our return journey to the Lodge via Mulo was every bit as rough as the trip coming out. Twice we paused because tires had gone flat under the strain. John fixed them on the spot, the inner tubes having been patched so often they looked like crazy quilts.

After a few hours of what seemed like life in a popcorn shaker, we arrived at the Lodge. John and Kona stayed in a cabin for the night, planning to return to their camp the next day. It was difficult to bid them farewell, and they were reluctant too. "The camp will be empty without you," said John.

Giny had Kona in her arms. "We must have been an awful bother to you," I said. "A photographer is always a nuisance—tumbling down cliffs and forgetting things."

"Being with you has meant more than I can tell you right now," said John sincerely. "Our paths have crossed once. I feel that they will again."

We shortened our farewell, inviting John and Kona

to visit us at our Sanctuary, and they promised that one day they would do so.

"Bless his heart," Giny said as she looked after Kona. "I can hardly let go of him."

There was more mail from Hi-Bub and Tony. The island was still a beehive of action. They wrote:

Dear Sam and Giny:

Your telegram arrived too late. Tony was lost when I received it. He went chasing after Zowie out near Vanishing Lake and the first thing he knew he didn't know anything. He was gone so long Zanie and I went looking for him. For two hours we kept walking and shouting until finally he answered—away out in the middle of the big swamp. We got him out of that all right, and then discovered that we were all lost! The sky was covered with a solid bank of gray clouds, so we couldn't see the sun and we didn't know north from up. I remembered you taught us that the top branch of a hemlock tree points east, so I found some hemlocks. What do you know? It works! We came out at the north end of our own lake and got home just as Tony was starting to bite off my ears. He hadn't had any food since morning. Don't worry about us, though. We had fun, and now I have hung a cowbell on Tony. The skunk odor is about worn off so I can't find him by that any more. I'll have to listen for him.

Love,
Hi-Bub

"You know," said Giny, "I am getting desperately homesick—for our cabin, for the animals, those boys and everything. How soon can we go back?"

"In about two days, if we work hard."

"Then let's work hard. It isn't that I'm tired of the Canyon country . . . it is just that . . ."

"I know, you want to go home!"

The next letter we opened was from Tony.

Dear Sam and Giny:

Hi-Bub says I must write this because I am the one who saw the whole business. Last night Andrea, the raccoon, came over with her six little problems. They are getting to the place where they won't always mind, and she has her troubles with them. We had quite a lot of tasty scraps for them and they sure put away a big dinner. They ate until they couldn't eat any more and then they wanted a siesta. I saw three of them go down the woodchuck's hole! I started to worry right away, for they could barely squeeze in the hole, and I couldn't picture how they were going to get out. They couldn't turn around as I saw it, and how could they back out? I had visions of importing a steamshovel to do some hurried excavating. Along about midnight Andrea roused herself and started to assemble her family. I'd give a lot to know just what goes on at such a time. I have seen her direct her mob before. Usually there isn't any sound that you can hear—they just pick up and go. Last night when she was ready, only three of the offspring showed up. She wasn't satisfied, and for the first time I heard her make a trilling sound. No answer. She did it again. No answer. Then she went all around searching and calling, wearing such a worried look. All this time I was picturing those three down in the hole slowly smothering.

Hi-Bub was writing some letters and I called him out for a conference. Should we start to dig or not? Next we watched Andrea go right to the hole. She sniffed in it and then tried to crawl in herself. The hole was much too small, but it was surprising how far she went in. Everything disappeared but her hind legs and tail. Presently she backed out. She knew her chillun were in there all right and she kept calling in a way that was a mixture of scolding and bawling.

We couldn't stand it any longer and were just starting for the pick and shovel when a woolly black-striped face peeked out of the woodchuck hole. The little fellow looked guilty—as if he had been caught in the jam jar. He had something coming and he knew it. Andrea leaped over to that hole and grabbed him by the head. She actually pulled him out of that hole, stretching his neck out about three inches. A second youngster poked his head out and he got treated the same way. By the time the third coon appeared Andrea had herself worked up into a lather. She jerked him out of there and gave him a trimming that he will never forget. Then she took her brood on the double-quick down to the lake and made them swim to the mainland.

We took a flashlight and looked into the woodchuck hole. Way down in there we could see a wide place. Apparently the coons knew all about this big underground room and they had gone to sleep down there. They won't do it again!

NEXT NEWS! (Twenty-four hours later) WOW! What a day this has been. We have been out at Somewhere Lake ever since early morning. We found more tracks of the stranger's big feet, and we found a red handkerchief someone had dropped. This all happens on the far side of the lake away from the trail. Someone is coming in from the west.

What do you suppose happened? Sleepy, Grumpy, and Dopey, or else some of the others, crawled right up in our laps. Yes, they did! We had been sitting beside the lake feeding them as we always do. They think nothing of taking bites of apples from our hands. But we began teasing them to come closer and closer until one of them climbed up on Hi-Bub's knees and took a nibble of cookie. Guess the beaver didn't know what he was doing, for when he looked around and saw that he was in Hi-Bub's lap, he flopped down and into the lake in a hurry. He came back a minute later though, or someone did, dripping wet and climbed back in Hi-Bub's lap. Then one came up to me. Within an hour we had them coming regularly.

I guess they had as much fun as we did, for they tried to bring as much water as possible and let it run all over us. We were soaking wet, but we had a swell time! The beavers are getting wonderful. They just take us for granted. One was dragging a stick along through the woods when we came on him, and he pulled it right across my feet. I helped him, and he said thank you—or at least he looked it!

Love,
Tony

P. S. Roll call at dinner tonight: Present, Zanie, Zowie and one wild fox, Zinnia and two wild skunks, three chipmunks, three red squirrels, thirty-nine red-winged blackbirds, seven blue jays, seven woodchucks, one porcupine (Salt), Tony, Hi-Bub. Absent: Zipper, dern her hide!

"Sam!" cried Giny. "Think of those beavers, working right at your feet, coming up in your lap. Think of those cute coons! Are you going to take me home, or must I start walking?"

"We're heading home all right!" I said with decision. "I want to know who is leaving those tracks at Somewhere Lake."

XXII

TONGUES AWAGGING

THE shortest distance between two points may be a straight line, but still it is a long way when you are going *home*. We went as straight from Grand Canyon to northern Wisconsin as roads would permit, but it seemed to us we would never get there. At last we had put the endless prairie states behind us, and we entered the fringes of the northern forests, passing close to the shores of little lakes. The world is a mixture of *visiting places* and *home*. Giny and I know of no region we do not love to visit, but *home* is our northern Wisconsin Sanctuary and to us it is supreme for the purpose.

We must have sounded like a cage full of monkeys when we landed at our island that sunny afternoon in late August. Tony and Hi-Bub had been advised by wire when we would arrive, and they had a boat awaiting us. On the boat seats spelled out in birch twigs were the words, "Welcome home, Sam and Giny!" As we rowed up to our pier, they came down to meet us. Such wild jabbering as took place! Everyone was talking and nobody listening. Zanie barked his part of the conversation and wagged his tail until his hind legs danced all around.

In spite of all the excitement, I studied Hi-Bub closely. What I saw led me to emit one of my best war whoops.

They all thought it was merely from the joy of arriving home, and I let it pass for that, but really it was provoked by the appearance of our lad. His eyes were sparkling with happiness, his face flushed with unrestrained excitement, and once more he was the atom bomb of life and enthusiasm we had known through the years. "The woods have done it!" I said to myself, and I emitted one more "WA-HOO!" that sent the lake shores to echoing.

"Oh, we're a couple of wrecks, a couple of wrecks!" panted Hi-Bub when at last we were in our cabin and calmed down to where conversation was possible. "What a day we put in!" He and Tony leaned against each other for support. "You see, we wanted to have everyone here to greet you," Hi-Bub went on. "Been planning it for days, but we got no co-operation. This morning they were all here—Zipper, Zowie, Zanie, Zinnia, Salt and Pepper, two extra deer and one extra skunk."

"And a bear!" put in Tony.

"A bear?" questioned Giny.

"Yes, a bear," insisted Hi-Bub. "Just before dawn we heard something big swimming and splashing north of the island. Went out with flashlights and caught sight of a bear just crawling out of the water on the west side of the island."

"We wanted to keep him for you, but we didn't have a chance," Tony managed to get in. "We said, 'here bear, here bear, nice bear,' but he kept on going."

They both talked at once, but we learned from the mingled jabbering that the bear ran the length of the island and immediately swam away to the south. Through our years at the island we have had many casual visitors like that. We believe the island is in line with a long-used migratory route, and for centuries has been a stopping place for all kinds of animals as they come through the area.

"That was 4:00 A.M.," bubbled Hi-Bub. "Our troubles started soon after that. We couldn't decide what was best to do in order to keep the animals here for you. If we gave them breakfast they might go away satisfied, if we didn't they might go looking for their own food. Then we decided to stuff them and maybe they would be so lazy they couldn't move."

"Wow, did we feed them!" sputtered Tony. "They must have thought it was their birthday. As fast as they cleaned up one batch of grub we brought them another. Zipper had three bottles of milk. Zowie had four servings of fox biscuit. Zinnia ate scraps until she looked like a white-striped balloon. Zanie ate something of everything."

"And then," cut in Hi-Bub, "and then, in place of going to sleep the way we planned for them, they all started leaving the island at the same time. Salt and Pepper began swimming to the south, and Tony waded in and shooed them back. I caught Zipper just leaving to the west and I picked her up and carried her ashore. Zowie went swimming out, and I caught up with him in the boat and brought him back. Zinnia started to swim too, but Zanie understood what was going on and he turned her around."

"It was a madhouse, I tell you." Tony was holding

his head. "We raced around this island until we were dizzy, pulling animals out of the water. We decided we would tire them out, but we were the ones that got exhausted. Even Zanie here had his tongue hanging out about a foot." Tony reached down and petted the dog who was sitting right beside him. We found later that this was the usual thing. Tony and Zanie were inseparable.

"Everyone slipped through our fingers except Zanie, and he's always on our side," concluded Hi-Bub. "Our reception for you is a total flop. What is that about 'the best laid plans of mice and men . . .?' "

"O.K., mouse!" Tony slapped him on the back. "We did our best anyway."

"Well, you're a couple of grand fellows, and we appreciate your good intentions," said Giny. "The animals will come back. Maybe it is best that we don't see everyone at once. The excitement might be too much for us."

"Oh, oh," burst out Hi-Bub, with sudden recollection. "We're forgetting something. Come on, Tony, you know we have learned to speak a piece."

"I'm not in the mood," said Tony, bashfully.

"Well, you get in the mood," warned Hi-Bub. "Or else I'll tell about the biscuits you made with varnish."

"You do, and I'll tell of the time you put kitchen cleanser in the soup."

"Don't fight, boys," I put in. "No doubt there is plenty for us to hear, but right now we want you to speak your piece. I am sure it is beautiful."

They bowed around for a while, whispering back and forth to refresh their memories about certain lines. Then they stood side by side, made stiff bows and began in traditional schoolboy diction:

"We've been so good, he and I;
To please Sam and Giny we try;
But now comes the day
When we get our pay.
Will you bake us a blueberry pie?"

"I'll do it!" cried Giny, applauding. "I'll do it right today. Do you have the berries?"

"We have everything!" said Tony. "Oh, how wonderful it will be to have a pie when we dare to eat the crusts!"

Giny baked a blueberry pie all right, and it was a masterpiece. I marvel at how she did it. Hi-Bub, Tony and I hung around the kitchen, and every move Giny made she bumped into one or the other. Everything she prepared we had to taste. She was showered with inexpert advice. We kept urging her to put more and more berries in the pie until the top crust bulged up like Mount Rainier. When the pie went into the oven and started its cooking routine, the top crust broke loose and floated around like a raft. It turned out well in spite of us.

"I don't want to infer that Hi-Bub isn't a good cook," said Tony as he raved over the gastronomic quality of the pie. "He is the finest can-opener I ever met. But some way on such delicacies as pies, he lacks that feminine touch!"

Hi-Bub didn't answer; his mouth was too full of pie.

During the evening all our wilderness zoo reported in except Zowie. Perhaps it was our imaginations enlivened by our desires in the matter, but we were convinced the animals knew us and were glad to see us. Zipper came up to nuzzle us, and Zinnia, still wet from the swim to our island, stayed at our very feet for a long time. Salt and Pepper put in a belated appearance. Zanie, of course, was expressing his joy at our return, though every few minutes he settled at Tony's feet, or if the opportunity came, jumped up in his lap. Obviously the two were welded together—that age-old perfect union of boy and dog.

The conversation before the grate fire ran late into the evening. Each one had so much to tell we finally agreed to abide by Roberts' Rules of Order to keep from having all talkers and no listeners. Tony told things on Hi-Bub, and Hi-Bub paid him back in kind. Tony's experience with the strange skunk was told and retold, and it lost nothing in the telling!

The boys listened intently to our account of the Western adventure. They drew from us every detail of our meeting with John Corn and Kona, and made us use frequently our brief vocabulary of Hopi words. The description of Z-Bar and our trip into the Canyon brought outbursts of laughter from them. I was discovering how much other people enjoyed my misery. This led me to overstate the difficulties encountered, in the interest of general happiness.

"I'd give my piece of blueberry pie to see you on that mule," roared Hi-Bub. "You're mighty selfish not to do it where more people could see you."

I just glared at him.

When we came to my debacle of the mountain-lion photography, the boys at first refused to believe it. "Sam wouldn't do that," they insisted.

"But he did!" affirmed Giny.

They then sentenced me to three days on bread and water. Most leniently they announced that the strict, punishing diet was in addition to my usual meals.

At this point we unwrapped the painting of the lioness and cubs. Both boys were intrigued with its beauty, but Hi-Bub was simply carried away. "No, I can't believe it!" he exclaimed. "I can't believe anything could be so wonderful." For the rest of the evening his eyes seldom left the canvas.

When our tongues were tired with wagging and it was time to get some rest, Hi-Bub and I went down to the pier to see if there was a display of northern lights. Giny and Tony were going over some verses he had written. Andrea and her six little coons were at the feeding station as we passed. We found that a faint glow of the aurora was playing along the horizon. Capella, the star that seems to belong to our Sanctuary, was semaphoring messages of beauty from its position just above the treetops. The air was vibrant with the calls of insects, tree toads and frogs.

For some time we stood in silence watching the nocturnal spectacle. Twice Hi-Bub moved as if to speak, but no words came out. I could sense his response to the beauty before us.

"Like it, my lad?" I questioned.

Hi-Bub didn't answer in words. He didn't need to. He was loving his surroundings with all his wonderful, boyish heart. I put my arm about his shoulders and said no more aloud. "Hold your gains, Hi-Bub," my private thoughts ran. "Don't trade your real self again for some false personality just to please the world. Sometimes we have to fight for the right, not fight people but wrong ideas. It is the way we mold and keep our ideals, it is the way we grow from boyhood to manhood. The Creator has entrusted you with a most precious character, one wherewith you can serve the world and find happiness for yourself. Let no opposing thoughts steal from you what God has given."

But Hi-Bub knew all this and more. Manliness was reaching forth from within him. He could not put it into words, but I was sure he would be forever expressing it in acts.

XXIII

SECRETS OF THE SECRETS

Tony and Hi-Bub evidenced a great deal of personal pride and ownership in the beavers of Somewhere Lake. They led us to this secluded haven with much ceremony. We reached the lake before sunrise on our first visit. Zanie went along, of course. He held close to Tony and did whatever Tony did. If the boy crept up to a tree and peered around it cautiously, the dog did too. If Tony crawled along flat to the ground, so did Zanie. When once the lake was in sight and the beavers active, our pup was at his best. One moment he would be staring at the flat-tails while he trembled with excitement. Then he would break into a doggy smile, looking around at each of us to see if we saw everything too, while he panted his enthusiasm.

"Do you see much difference in the lake?" asked Hi-Bub.

"An amazing difference!" exclaimed Giny. "The water is much higher and it is so clear."

"Yes, we can see the beavers swimming 'way down deep," commented Hi-Bub. "There are four food caches now, and every time we come we see them bringing in material."

The boys led us to the edge of the lake. At first the several beavers that were swimming about slapped the water with their tails and dived. However, they were soon up again and approaching us cautiously. There was one big food cache at the point where the trail comes to the lake. The clever animals had brought in fair-sized limbs of the aspen tree, forcing the big end of the limbs into the soil at the bottom of the lake. Large-sized stones had been placed on these branches to hold them down. Layer after layer of branches and stones would be deposited in these caches until a great pile of brush had accumulated. Then when winter days come, the beaver will swim under the ice and feed on the bark and leaves of this food storage.

"Isn't it awfully cold for them in that water during the winter?" Hi-Bub shivered at the thought. "You tell me it gets fifty below zero here sometimes."

"Yes, it does get that cold," I replied. "But, Hi-Bub, the water under the coating of ice is comparatively warm. It must be thirty-two degrees above zero or higher, or it would be solid ice. Their fur is thick, their bodies warm, and so a swim in thirty-two-degree water is like a dip in a tropical pool for them."

"But it would take a long time for them to swim over and feed that way under the ice," put in Tony. "What do they do—take oxygen from the water like a fish?"

"No, the beaver is a lung-breather. He needs air, just as we do. He can hold his breath for at least ten minutes and perhaps longer. Then usually there are air bubbles imprisoned under the ice, and he may come to one of them for breathing."

"Now, one point you can clear up for me," said Giny.

"When he is chewing at this brush under water, how come he doesn't get his mouth flooded with water?"

"Because his lips meet behind his front teeth," I explained. "He can seal off the rest of his mouth and chew as long as his breath holds out."

"His ears?" queried Hi-Bub.

"Both his ears and his nostrils are equipped with valves. These are operated by voluntary muscular action and close against the water. He is perfectly leakproof when he goes down under, you may be sure of that."

Our conversation was interrupted as Hi-Bub noted one of the animals swimming toward us deep under the surface. We could see him plainly. His streamlining was most apparent. His body looked like a model for a modern submarine. His nose was pointed forward, his front feet folded neatly to his body so as to offer little resistance to the water, his hind feet with their big webbed toes were propelling him, and his flat tail was acting as a rudder. Sometimes his tail works in propelling motion too, but this one was using it only for guidance.

"How fast can he go?" whispered Tony.

"He is not such a fast swimmer," I answered. "He has been timed at two miles per hour, though some students think he can go a little faster."

The beaver emerged suddenly at the water's edge, about twenty feet from where we stood.

"It's Dopey!" exclaimed Hi-Bub.

"Nope, it's Doc!" argued Tony.

"It's Dopey, I tell you."

"How do you know?"

"I just know it's Dopey, that's all!"

"Well—" Tony was unconvinced—"it's Doc!"

Whether it was Dopey, Doc, Sneezy, Sleepy or who, it was a beautiful animal, and seeing him so intimately was a thrilling experience for all of us. Zanie went into a spasm of delight. He pranced back and forth in front of the unperturbed creature, giving muffled barks of welcome.

The beaver shook himself free of water and stretched his head high, displaying the four sharp orange-colored teeth at the front of his mouth.

"Oh, do you need a change of tooth paste!" said Hi-Bub softly.

"Don't worry about his teeth," I commented. "Whether dentists approve of that color or not, those are good teeth. In fact, they are a most vital part of his equipment. He does all the cutting of trees with them."

"Doesn't he wear them out doing that sort of thing?" asked Tony.

"No, to the contrary, his teeth grow so fast, if he does not keep up his cutting they become too long and hold his mouth open. That is why beavers sometimes cut trees they do not need for food or building. They must keep those teeth from overgrowing."

Dopey or Doc put on a fine show for us that morning. As if he realized he was exhibit *A* of a scientific demonstration, he performed his toilet before us. With an elaborate motion, he swung his tail forward and sat upon it. This position seems to aid in the discharge of oil from the glands near the base of his tail, a substance which is applied to his fur to resist the action of water. Here he took to combing his fur. The second toe on each hind foot is split, forming a "comb," and he uses them for that purpose.

"Dopey, do you want my powder puff?" asked Giny.

"Towel?" asked Hi-Bub.

"Lipstick? Rouge? Mirror?" added Tony.

But the beaver kept right on, not even noticing Zanie, who was stretched out three feet from him, fascinated at what he saw. His toilet finished, Dopey came to us for a bite of apple. By way of demonstration Hi-Bub teased him up into his lap. Then the interesting creature waddled back to the lake, Zanie following him right into the water. The two animals swam about for awhile, the beaver obviously making sport of the dog.

Day after day we returned to our beaver colony. The animals were settling down to work, preparing for the coming winter. Every day wonderful things were happening, and we did not want to miss a single development. Besides, the time was rapidly approaching when Hi-Bub and Tony must return to their schools, and they wanted to see as much of this beaver land as possible.

Trees were falling before the cutting of the beavers. We could see no evidence that the animals fell the trees in a chosen direction. The aspens were crisscrossed on the ground, some in such a way as to be of no use to the beavers, and a number of their cuttings had leaned against neighboring trees. The beaver is such a fascinating and mysterious animal that the tendency among nature enthusiasts is to credit him with a lot of purpose and plan he does not have. To dispute popular fallacies, the beaver does not cause trees to fall a certain way, he does not use his tail as a trowel, he does not suck the air out of sticks to make them sink, he does not use muskrats as "slaves" to do his work, he does not drive stakes with his tail. There is enough evidence of the cleverness of this remarkable creature without inventing things.

At one point along the shores of Somewhere Lake, we saw the beginning of the beaver's most remarkable accomplishments. The Seven Secrets had begun a canal! It was about five inches deep, a foot wide, and fifty feet long when we first discovered it. Already its purpose was plain. They were digging it toward a fine stand of aspen trees 200 feet back from the lake. They had done some cutting among these trees, but apparently had learned that it was a big task to drag the material to the water. Hence they concluded that water transportation would be easier. They understood that water wouldn't run uphill, so their canal was following the lowland. In future days they would scoop out their little waterway until it held water about eight inches deep, and in this they would float their cuttings down for use in their home building. These animal engineers have been known to build a canal 750 feet long.

One morning Hi-Bub and I went alone to the lake, and we witnessed something that has been seen by very few people. Every student knows beavers cut trees, and from studying the cuttings they reason out how it must have been done. But seldom have I met anyone who has actually seen a beaver at this work. Beavers use the nighttime for their labor, and this, coupled with their alertness and shyness and especially their reticence at being caught away from the safety of their pond, makes observation of them extremely difficult.

Hi-Bub and I arrived at the lake while the shades of night still hung in the woods. Zanie, refusing to leave Tony, stayed behind, whining and looking after us, knowing full well where we were going.

We paused back of the shore-line trees as was our custom in approaching the lake, to look about for anything unusual. There were two deer this eventful morning, and we remained concealed while we watched them slowly work their way along the shore and then turn back into the woods.

"I hear something," whispered Hi-Bub.

I caught the sound too, an intermittent chewing noise that came from a point rather close down the shore. We edged forward until we could get our binoculars on the spot where the sound originated. There stood a beaver (Dopey, Hi-Bub said it was), working on an aspen tree that was about six inches in diameter and had already been cut halfway through.

"Hi-Bub," I said softly, trying to curb my own excitement. "Watch every bit of this, remember what you see. This is a rare opportunity."

The morning light was strengthening, and we could see the beaver plainly. How long he had been working on this tree we had no way of knowing, but a tree that size has been cut in a single night by one beaver. We noted that this work was constant, but it was not frantic. Nature's creatures seem never to work under strain. They are calm, deliberate, persistent, but not hurried. We saw him take one large chip after another from the widening gash in the tree. He cut first at one end, then at the other, then inserted his teeth in the center and pried the chip out. At times he stepped back from his work, actually looking toward the top of the tree as if surveying its tendencies. Then he would resume his cutting, always the same method of taking out large chips.

Once he stopped his work and fed for a few moments on some grass near at had. Following this, he calmly made his toilet, as had the one we witnessed several days previously. Other beavers passed near him, but none aided him. The cutting of this tree was his sole assignment. We kept our glasses on him for nearly two hours and then saw the tree topple over. Without hesitating, the worker started cutting off the branches. Now other beavers joined in the task, both in cutting and dragging the material into the lake. At no time did we see any beaver haul away a log or branch that another had cut. The law or custom seemed to be to cut and carry one's own.

In an hour's time the tree had been completely cut and the beavers disappeared into the lake. We went to the spot and took notes on the chips. Some of them were five inches long and half an inch thick! Where the trunk of the tree had been cut up there were piles of chips by which we could measure the length of the log sections. Toward the butt of the trunk two logs had been

cut three feet long; higher up, these sections measured four and five feet each.

"Never forget that experience, Hi-Bub," I commented. "You and I have been treated to a secret of the Secrets."

"I still wonder if I am dreaming," he answered, his face beaming.

In successive visits we saw the first work the animals did on their houses. There were three under construction. These consisted of piles of mud, grass and sticks, arranged in a compact, strong mass. Each house will be enlarged until it rises above the surface of the water. The beaver tunnels up into the mound from the bottom of the pond, ultimately making a living room for himself and family above water level. This chamber may be as much as six feet across and two feet high. It will be perfectly sealed and plastered with mud, but an air vent will be left in the top. It is a marvel of planning, giving the beaver protection from the weather and such enemies as the wolf and wildcat. Since he feeds under water and enters his home from the bottom of the pond, he is well protected from all predators, except the trapper.

Somewhere Lake has one trickling stream as an outlet. Our Seven Secrets apparently decided they wanted the lake level raised, so they made a dam in this stream. We saw the first moves of this construction work. They placed green branches in the stream, the large ends of the limbs facing upstream, the leafy ends downstream. They forced these to stay in place by pushing them into the mud, then placing stones on them. Moss, mud, logs and water-soaked sticks were added until the dam was nearly two feet high and thirty feet long. This ultimately would raise the lake level two feet, so the houses were planned accordingly. Controlling the height of the water by means of the dam was a great advantage to the creatures, as now they knew just where to make their living rooms so they would not be flooded; nor would the water get so low that the young beavers of the next spring would have a hard time getting up into the home.

We had nearly forgotten about the stranger who had visited our lake. Tony and Hi-Bub pointed out the tracks, but they had been almost completely washed away by rains. It was the afternoon before Hi-Bub and Tony were to return to their city homes that we had our next shock at Somewhere Lake. We made a quick trip out there so the boys would have one of those last-time looks at the place they had learned to love so well. As we sat watching the evening shades gather in the forest, we heard the breaking of twigs on a hillside on the far side of the lake. Thinking it was a deer coming, we directed our binoculars to the area. To our surprise a man walked out of the woods and up to the shore.

Anxiously I studied the figure. The light was not good, but there was no question—it was Bill! Bill, the trapper, had discovered the Seven Secrets of Somewhere Lake. "What now?" I asked myself.

XXIV

SURPRISE!

THE brilliant, alluring days of Indian summer rested upon the north country. The forest was dressed in a cloak of many colors. The scarlet of maples, the orange of aspens, the yellow of birches and basswoods, the rich maroon of oaks, all mingled with the dark green of pines, hemlocks, balsams and cedars in dazzling array. Wild geese were winging their way southward in V formations, their cries adding charm to the scene.

Our two lads had gone southward too and were now caught up in school routine. Each boy bore a purposeful gift as he left. Hi-Bub was speechless with delight when Giny and I gave him the painting of the mountain lion and her cubs. "Hang it where you see it every day, Hi-Bub," I requested in presenting it. "It will help you recall lessons of this summer, and help you hold your gains."

"If I let myself drift away again, will you please set me down on a porcupine?" he answered, his eyes devouring the painting.

Tony had a gift too. There was only one thing it could be. It was the only thing he wanted, and *it* wanted him. So we gave Tony and Zanie to each other! As the train pulled out, the two boys and the dog were on the platform, looking out at us and waving, the boys with their hands,

Zanie with his tongue and tail. Tony had a yard in which Zanie could run. He had squirrels and birds coming to a feeding station, and the dog could take care of them.

The island seemed empty to Giny and me when our two lads and Zanie were gone. However, nature did not give us time to cultivate loneliness. The forest world was preparing for winter.

Zinnia seldom visited the island as the fall began. She needed a much larger area in order to gather the variety of food she needed. Likely she had already selected a spot suitable for hibernation where she could dream the winter away.

Zowie was an irregular visitor. Occasionally he would put in an appearance, and a beautiful appearance it was, though we could see he was taking to the wilds. Now that Zanie was gone, Zowie had a chance to grow some hair in his tail, and it was about the size of a feather duster. He was unvarying in his interest in us, however. Several times we came on him far back in the woods. Always he behaved in a most friendly way, staying near us, circling us, and usually touching our fingers with his nose in greeting before he trotted away. Once we saw this fox ten miles from our lake.

Zipper was the most regular guest at our island. There were periods when she was gone for three or four days, but presently she would appear at our door begging for her favorite tidbits. She still fed on the bottle at times, but actually she looked embarrassed and self-conscious when she did. She knew she had outgrown such infantile things, but she still liked the idea. When the bottle was offered her, she would lick the nipple, assume a silly expression and take it, rolling her eyes at us as if saying, "All right, just to please you I'll do it, but don't you tell anyone."

Somewhere Lake continued to be the center of interest. Our camera was in constant use there, and I took off the lens cap and left it off! How those Seven Secrets crept into our affections, how important they became to us, and how gripping their wise ways of living!

We just presumed there were still seven, though we never saw them all at one time. The fact that at last we had gained permission to look into the inner workings of a beaver colony was the important thing. We saw them enlarging their food caches in the lake until the top portions reached above the surface of the water. They strengthened their dam, allowing a low point at one side to remain, and there a small waterfall developed, its voice adding soft music to the forest. Their houses were large now, with walls thick and strong, well prepared for the winter.

Constantly I was haunted by the knowledge that Bill, the trapper, knew of the colony. Toward the end of the winter when beaver fur was heavy and beautiful would come the trapping season. Was he planning a harvest of these creatures? Undoubtedly this was true, for the beaver pelt is one of the most valuable of the forest, and to the professional trapper a fur is a fur, whether it is on a pet animal or a stranger, and it is worth so much money —that is all that matters.

We were nearing the time when we must leave on a

lecture tour. November changed the face of the forest. Before sharp-edged north winds, deciduous leaves lost their brilliance, were shaken from the trees and drifted to the ground. Our beavers worked more industriously than ever. Their canal was now 200 feet long, and we saw them using it to float material down to the lake.

The whole operation at Somewhere Lake was inspiring to see. It was so complete, so well planned. Their community operated as a perfect democracy. Each worker did his share, did it well, without grumbling or imposing on the rights of his fellows. There was no boss, no director, but all were inspired to labor for the common good. Also, we noted evidence that they were happy creatures. We saw them engage in brief tussles together, a form of play that evidenced good humor. Although beavers are known to fight one another on occasions, we saw none of it at Somewhere Lake. They were fine, intelligent, admirable forest citizens and they deserved to live.

"I must do something about it," I said to Giny one day. "It is certain that Bill is planning to trap them. He may not even wait for the trapping season. He knows all the tricks of that cruel trade, and I doubt if one will escape him."

"What can we do?" she asked.

"I'm going straight to Bill and talk to him about it!" I finally said to Giny.

"But he has a right to trap them, as long as he does it in season," she said, distressed. "He makes his living trapping animals. Do you think he would listen to an appeal?"

"That is the point," I replied. "It is his living, and I am going to offer him the top price for those furs if he just lets them alone. It is the money that he wants."

"But do you suppose you could trust him to let them alone even if you paid him?"

"I'm not sure, but it is the only thing I know to do."

We planned to go to Bill's cabin on the first rainy day when we could not work at photography. The trip was not necessary. Bill came to see us. I saw him out on the lake trolling, slowly working his way toward our island. He landed and greeted us cordially. Zipper was home that day, and Bill was right happy to see her.

"She's fine," he declared. "Guess the boys took good care of her."

"Yes, Bill, they did."

"Fine boys!"

"Yes."

Our conversation was apart from our thoughts, however. Both Giny and I were trying to think out the best way to approach Bill on the beaver problem. Should we appeal to friendship? Should we try to find that level of decency which must be in every man and strive to awaken him to a higher mode of living? Had he enough admiration for Tony and Hi-Bub that their love for the beavers might influence him?

"We-ell," Bill said, drawing in a big breath. "I just dropped in to tell you good-by."

"Nice of you, Bill," said Giny, "but we are not going for a few days."

"No . . . but I am."

"You are going away?" Giny and I exchanged glances.

"Yes . . . I guess you didn't know that I re-enlisted in the army. Just got my call."

"Bill, I didn't know you wanted more military service," I said, trying to figure out what all this meant.

"Well, when I came out I thought I was through, but I found I was always kind of wishing for it again. After all, it is a carefree life, and I'll see lots of places that I couldn't see any other way."

"When do you go?" I asked, mean enough to hope it would be soon.

"Tomorrow," answered Bill. "That is why I had to see you today."

One idea after another was flashing through my mind. Bill was going and this was good, for he wanted to go, but did this take the threat away from our beavers? His father and brother would be left behind, and did they know of the colony at Somewhere Lake?

But Bill was talking. "Before I go there is a secret I want to tell you."

"A secret? I love secrets," I said.

"Yes, and do I have your promise not to tell anyone?"

"You do, Bill, providing what you tell me is legal and my keeping the secret doesn't harm anyone."

"You're cautious, Sam," laughed Bill. "No, this won't harm anyone, and it's legal, and I know you'll want to do it."

"All right, I promise."

"I know a place not far away where there is a lake full of beavers!"

"You do, Bill?" I exclaimed, acting pretty well, I thought.

"Yes, and the funny thing is they are not afraid. I see them in daylight, and I get right up to them."

"I can hardly believe it, Bill. Do you want to tell me where it is?"

"Yes, have you got a section map?" he asked. While I obtained a map, he kept talking. "I found them while I was running a line. One of the best colonies I ever saw. I went there half a dozen times. Oh, man, how they are cutting and building! I made up my mind I wouldn't tell a soul. You know," he said confidentially, "there are a lot of fellows that would like to find a bunch of beavers like that. They would trap them out in no time, probably wouldn't even wait for the season for fear someone else would beat them to it. I kept it a secret."

"Good! Bill—that is, were you figuring to take them yourself?"

"Well, they are worth a lot of money, but I won't be here when the time comes. Anyway, I've been having lots of fun watching them. Now, I am going to tell you where they are, for you can make pictures of them."

"Don't even your father and Ed know?" asked Giny.

"No, those beavers wouldn't last a month if they knew. Nobody knows, but me! Now look, here is the section line. I've been coming in from the west, but maybe you can find it from this side...." And Bill proceeded to show me the exact location of Somewhere Lake!

"I was wanting to tell Hi-Bub and Tony," he said, winking. "They like animals so well, but I was afraid.

Boys do a lot of talking, you know, and they might tell someone in town. Then, good-by beavers!"

"Bill," I said, after he had shared his "beaver secret" with us fully, "what would seven beaver skins be worth?"

He named a figure with a shake of his head, indicating it was a right good sum in his eyes. "Hope nobody collects it," he added.

I wrote out a check for something more than the amount. "Bill," I said, "you will be serving us by being in the army. In appreciation we want you to take this gift."

Bill looked at the check, then took it hesitantly. "Looks mighty good," he said. "I don't have very much to go on."

When Bill left, his last words called back from the boat were, "Be sure and keep our secret!"

XXV

THE GREATEST GIFT

IT WAS the day before Christmas. Giny and I stood looking through our cabin window at the steady drift of huge snowflakes that had been falling for more than twenty-four hours. In the absence of any wind, the flakes remained exactly where they fell. They were heaped up on logs and stumps, they outlined the limbs of deciduous trees, they gathered in mounds on balsams, making these trees look like white ghosts frozen in the midst of a grotesque dance. Our cabin was but a cave in a huge snow drift.

"Looks like our wish had come true," remarked Giny.

"It has . . . we are snowbound at last," I agreed. "It will be at least four days before snowplows can open the roads."

"What a perfect time for it to happen!" she exclaimed delightedly. "Imagine, snowbound at our home on Christmas!"

The storm was so heavy we could not see more than fifty yards from our cabin. Near at hand stood our covered feeding station where our eleven chickadees and four nuthatches were helping themselves alternately to the seeds and suet we kept available. Let Giny or me step from the cabin door and these birds would be on us in an instant, perching on our heads, shoulders and hands. They were little feathered notes of joy on the winter landscape.

We talked of our forest friends. Since our return from the city for a winter sojourn at our island Sanctuary, we had seen but two living creatures other than the birds. Once on a snowshoe hike we came upon Zowie. We knew him by his actions—but how different he looked. His red coat was lighter in shade, but much thicker, making him seem double his real size. His tail was bushy, really the loveliest I had ever seen. Maybe the treatment Zanie gave it had some healthful properties. The beautiful fox circled us as he had in earlier days, showing obvious interest, but he did not come up to us. He leaped gracefully through the snow up to the top of a little hill and stood there looking back at us.

Zipper came to the island. Tracks in the snow indicated she was doing this regularly, and that an undetermined number of wild companions were coming with her.

Once we snowshoed back to Somewhere Lake. At first sight there was not a sign of life. Two feet of snow covered the lake, the beaver houses rising up like igloos. But as we neared one of the houses we noticed a little plume of vapor rising from it. It was from the breath of our Secrets. Down in there they were, sending out their "hellos" in this manner. Closer inspection of the other houses revealed the same evidence. So far, they were all right. No one had discovered them. Bill was honest with us. He was keeping our secret—and his.

"It is time for our Christmas cards," said Giny, happy

at the thought. "What a wonderful day to be reminded of our friends!"

It has been our custom to set aside a time on the day before Christmas for reading and appreciating Christmas cards. We love these greetings that come at this season, and we find that we can get full pleasure out of them only by dedicating a specific period to this purpose.

We read the messages and studied the beautiful decorations on the cards. Some were from friends with whom we were in constant contact, some were from people from whom we heard only at Christmas time. Zipper, Zowie, Zanie and Zinnia got almost as many greetings as we did. The Seven Secrets were not forgotten. Hi-Bub named everybody and everything to which he wanted his greetings extended, and his list filled a full page. Tony scribbled a verse on his:

> How happy you must be to be there!
> I know you have plenty to see there;
> I'm too far away,
> That's all I can say;
> I wish, oh, I wish you had me there.

Zanie sent a card too, with the aid of Tony. It showed a picture of the grand little pup, and as signature Tony had inked Zanie's foot and made a print at the bottom of the card.

For several hours we were opening cards, talking of the fine people who had sent them and of the fineness that is really in all people. Then Giny picked up one post-marked at an Arizona town of which we had never heard. As she read it, she burst forth joyfully, "Sam, look what a Christmas present we have!" Then: "Oh, this is won-derful!"

"What is it?" I asked, affected by her excitement.

"Oh!" she exclaimed, reading on to herself.

"Tell me what it is!" I begged.

She finished reading the message to herself, occasion-ally giving a delighted chuckle while I watched with much the same attitude Zanie has when he is begging for a bone.

"Sit comfortably, relax," she said at last, looking at me. "And if you don't say this is the best Christmas present you ever received, I will toss you out into a snowdrift."

"If you don't share that with me quickly, I'll jump out in a snowdrift voluntarily," I declared.

"Well, to begin with, this is signed 'Polimana.' "

"Polimana? You mean John's Polimana?"

"Yes."

Now I was so excited I rose to my feet. "Read!" I de-manded, "read, before I start walking on the ceiling."

She read slowly, looking at me frequently to see if I was properly attentive:

"Greetings to you two blessed people up in your north-ern home. I want to thank you for your kindness to my son and my husband. I know he has told you our story. Here is another chapter. I found I could not live without my family and I returned. John and Kona are so kind and forgiving. We are going to work out our problem together. . . ."

"Ya-hoo!" I screamed. Giny flashed a reproving look at me and continued:

"We have an opportunity to take a small ranch. John can continue his painting. We shall be reasonably close to a city where, I am sure, he may someday resume his work in architecture. Knowing you has meant so much to Kona. He will never forget you and neither will John— nor I.

Most sincerely,
Polimana.

Giny looked at me and I at her. "Excuse me, I think I'll feed the chickadees," I said in a weak voice. I stepped out the front door and the birds fluttered to me. The large snowflakes brushed past my face as they fell, and a few tears accompanied them to the ground.